THREE KINGS OF WARKA

THREE KINGS OF WARKA
Enmerkar, Lugalbanda, Gilgamesh
Myths from Mesopotamia

Retold by Fran Hazelton
Introduction by Stephanie Dalley
Illustrations by Eleanor Allitt

THE
ENHEDUANNA
SOCIETY

The Enheduanna Society
Box 36855, 1A Tagore House
Glenloch Road, London NW3 4BU

First published in 2012 by the Enheduanna Society

British Library Cataloguing in Publication data
A catalogue record of this book is available from the British Library

ISBN 978-0-9554330-2-3

Designer Jennifer Iles
Editor Ros Sales
Editorial Assistants Ziad Halub & Zoë Bratis
Consultant Editor Viv Croot
Typeset by InterOffice Communications in Adobe Garamond
Printed and bound in Great Britain

Contents

Acknowledgements

Any retelling of stories from Mesopotamian mythology has to be based on translations of the original Sumerian and Akkadian texts. The translations this retelling owes most to are those of Professor Thorkild Jacobsen, Dr Jeremy Black, Dr Graham Cunningham, Dr Eleanor Robson, Dr Gábor Zólyomi, Dr Herman Vanstiphout, Professor Andrew George, Dr Stephanie Dalley and Professor Benjamin R. Foster.

The process of taking the stories off the pages of these translations, through the art of oral storytelling, was a key part of the three-year **Discover Mesopotamia through Storytelling** project organised by the Enheduanna Society and funded mainly by the Heritage Lottery Fund. This process would not have been possible without my fellow Zipang storyteller June Peters and Zipang harpist Tara Jaff. We were supported by our manager Liqaa Yousef, new Zipang storytellers Badia Obaid, Laura Collins and Nico Pollen, and oud-player Mazin Emad. Essential to the process were the many volunteer helpers and 350 project participants.

The Iraqi Association and the Humanitarian Dialogue Foundation enabled the Enheduanna Society to take the **Discover Mesopotamia through Storytelling** project to a wider Iraqi audience. The British Institute for the Study of Iraq and the Unity Theatre Trust gave valued support that helped the project get off the ground. The Poetry Café in Covent Garden provided a suitable and supportive setting for Mesopotamian storytelling workshops.

The Mesopotamia galleries of the British Museum provided clues to the mythology in the material culture of ancient Iraq. Some of the objects in those galleries are the subjects of the illustrations in *Three Kings of Warka*. These are either drawings by Eleanor Allitt or photographs courtesy of the Trustees of the British Museum. The photograph of Mount Nimush taken in 2011 is courtesy of Dr Karen Radner.

Fran Hazelton
London, 2012

Map of Iraq

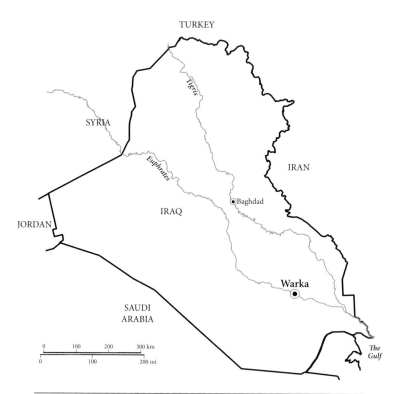

Warka, the site of the ancient city of Uruk, is located on the east side of the River Euphrates, about 30 km east of As-Samawah, capital city of the Al-Muthanna governorate.

Preface

The purpose of this written retelling of the Enmerkar, Lugalbanda and Gilgamesh stories is to have a record of how they were understood and developed by the storytellers and participants in the **Discover Mesopotamia through Storytelling** project (2009-2012).

The project participants provided ears and imaginations to receive the stories as they travelled from the storytellers' mouths in spoken words. They retold the stories themselves in groups or as solo storytellers. They took the stories away to tell to others. They found visual clues to the stories in the objects displayed in the Mesopotamia galleries at the British Museum. These objects included the clay tablets on which the stories were originally written by hand in cuneiform script.

For this end-of-project book, the stories have been typeset in the Roman alphabet after being amply retold by word of mouth. As in ancient times, the stories change with every retelling, yet the more they change the more they stay the same. This written retelling tries to strike a balance between two objectives. One is to make the stories accessible to anyone who can read an English newspaper. The other is to convey their startling originality.

THREE KINGS OF WARKA

Introduction

The Sumerian city Unug, modern Warka, was one of the most ancient cities in lower Mesopotamia. It boasted three famous kings, whose deeds are celebrated in these stories. According to the first story retold in this book, one of them invented writing, a claim apparently supported by the discovery on the site of very early written records. They are clay tablets inscribed with signs that developed into the cuneiform script. That way of writing, so strange to us now, recorded the earliest Sumerian legends nearly a thousand years after its invention. We think that these tales were told for centuries before they were written down on clay. This makes them especially suitable for modern storytellers.

Were those three kings historical people? The answer to this question is still uncertain. The earliest writing is several hundred years earlier than the supposed lifetime of the kings, and the stories were written down centuries later. But the first two tales reflect the trading expeditions of Early Dynastic Mesopotamia to eastern cities in present-day Iran, and the story of Gilgamesh reflects expeditions westwards, in the region of modern Lebanon, several centuries later.

The stories tell us about society in early Mesopotamia. The king from his throne in his palace ruled with a sceptre symbolising his power; he sent his messengers to negotiate trade deals backed up by threat of force. Gods and goddesses still lived on the earth, for they had not yet withdrawn to heaven, and their appetites—anger, delight in food and drink, lust and vanity—were similar to those of mortals, although only a deity could determine destinies and act as patron of a king and his city.

No opportunity for lavish feasting was overlooked, with fish, geese, eggs, cream, cheese, cucumbers and beer; this contrasted with an ever-present fear of famine. Hunting, military expeditions and magic were all used to keep chaos, enmity and evil at bay. Fine garments and jewellery showed off the importance of individuals, mortal and divine, so exotic foreign goods must be won: lapis lazuli from distant mines; carnelian, gold and silver, copper and tin; rare stone for statues; timber for doors and roof beams; even the skilled craftsmen to create some of the wonderful objects that are found in Mesopotamia and Iran from time to time. The citizens of Unug were proud of their prosperous city.

Lively speeches bring out the characters of the heroes. These are no cardboard men, but humans with ambitions and frailties. A rich store of brilliant similes lends colour to the Sumerian stories, many of them reflecting the countryside, whether the marshes of southern Iraq where fish and birds abound, or the mountains where wolves and lions prowl.

In the Akkadian story of Gilgamesh, a strong man meets his match and discovers his own limitations. Arrogance and ambition are tempered by hardship and the death of a beloved friend, by regret and by anger against fate. The story begins and ends by emphasising the fact that it was written down, and that the city of Uruk—Sumerian Unug—is where it began and ended.

The *Epic of Gilgamesh* developed from a melting pot of different, much shorter stories about the hero, many of them written in Sumerian at an earlier date. Fran Hazelton understands that the practice of stringing together and blending from ancient times can be continued very effectively to fill in some of the gaps in our cuneiform texts. So she uses versions of another story, *Gilgamesh and Humbaba*, to show the monster, Humbaba, in a sympathetic light. By blending in the story *Inana and the Bull of Heaven*, she includes Gilgamesh's musician singing with his lyre, reminding us that music was used in storytelling. When Utnapishtim, survivor of the Flood, tells of his escape, she includes material from the *Epic of Atrahasis* to create a seamless narrative.

While remaining faithful to the original texts, immersed in the ancient culture over many years, she has produced a retelling of real literary merit. Her interactive work for Zipang has given her a deep understanding of how to tell a story that fills the gaps in incomplete texts.

This book is a remarkable achievement that allows a wide readership to enjoy three of the best tales of ancient Mesopotamia.

Stephanie Dalley
Oxford, 2012

Enmerkar

*Enmerkar was the first mythical king of the ancient city that is now an archaeological site in southern Iraq known as Warka. This city's founders and original inhabitants were Sumerians, who named it Unug. It flourished from about 4000 BCE for nearly five thousand years and was twice the size of ancient Athens. It had a six-mile city wall and two city centres. One was the Eana district, which contained the house of the city deity, *Inana. The other was brick-built Kulaba, which was the centre of royal power. In the languages of Mesopotamian mythology—Sumerian and Akkadian—the word for deity is dingir and the names of deities are prefixed with the dingir sign, as in *Inana.*

*The Enmerkar story tells how the first diplomatic letter came to be written and how trade began between Unug and Aratta—the place in the mountains that had raw materials absent in the fertile lowlands. These hugely significant historical developments are explained in the story as a contest between the king of Unug, Enmerkar, and the lord of Aratta, Ensouggirana, about which of them is *Inana's beloved chosen one.*

Two important characters in the story are nameless. These are the messengers who run back and forth between Aratta and Unug through

1

the Zabu mountains. The story starts when Ensouggirana summons his messenger and gives him a challenging message to take to Enmerkar.

'Messenger, go to the city of Unug and say this to its king. "If you, Enmerkar, will do me the honour of submitting to me, this is how it can be for you and for me. You can live with ✶Inana in the Eana, in her House of the Skies in Unug, and I will live with her in the Ezagina, her House of Lapis Lazuli in Aratta. You can lie with ✶Inana on a flowery bed and I will lie with her on a bejewelled bed. You can meet ✶Inana in your dreams at night and I will meet her in bright daylight. It is true that you, Enmerkar, have barley to fatten your geese and I, Ensouggirana, without rain do not. However, I will collect the goose eggs and goslings in baskets and cook them in my pots. The goose eggs and goslings will be served with the rest of the geese at a feast in the mountains hosted by me. The guests at this feast will be the lords of the Land, who do me the honour of submitting to me." Go now, messenger!'

Ensouggirana's messenger charged from Aratta like a wild boar and flew like a falcon. He left at dawn to reach Unug by dusk. He disappeared into the mountains like the flocks of small birds that swarm in the mornings and at midnight. He stopped and stood still like a throw-stick, then dashed away like a large and sleek mountain donkey. He roared like a lion in the fields at daybreak, sped like a wolf running off with a lamb and made an impression wherever he went through spaces narrow and wide. When he entered the city of Unug he went straight to the throne-room and presented himself to Enmerkar.

'My master, Ensouggirana, the lord of Aratta, sends you a message.'

'What does he say?'

'He says this. "If you, Enmerkar, will do me the honour of submitting to me, this is how it can be for you and for me. You can live with *Inana in the Eana, in her House of the Skies in Unug, and I will live with her in the Ezagina, her House of Lapis Lazuli in Aratta. You can lie with *Inana on a flowery bed and I will lie with her on a bejewelled bed. You can meet *Inana in your dreams at night and I will meet her in bright daylight. It is true that you, Enmerkar, have barley to fatten your geese and I, Ensouggirana, without rain do not. However, I will collect the goose eggs and goslings in baskets and cook them in my pots. The goose eggs and goslings will be served with the rest of the geese at a feast in the mountains hosted by me. The guests at this feast will be the lords of the Land, who do me the honour of submitting to me." What is your reply, Enmerkar?'

Enmerkar was the son of the sun dingir *Utu, the lord of brick-built Kulaba and the king of the city of Unug. He had a reply for

3

Ensouggirana. As he spoke to the messenger he slowly patted a lump of wet clay until it became a smooth, flat tablet.

Enmerkar's bullish reply leaves Ensouggirana speechless

'Messenger, say this to your master. "You, Ensouggirana, may live with *Inana in her House of Lapis Lazuli in Aratta but I live with her when she comes down to earth from the skies. You may sleep with *Inana on a bed bedecked with jewels but I lie on her scented flowery bed when it glistens, blossoms and blooms. When *Inana is with me, two lions chase each other back and forth all night long as we take our far journey together. *Utu does not rise to shine on my crown when I am with *Inana. As the Anzud bird cries out to his chick so *Inana cries out to me when I go to her. When I go to her again she coos. *Inana lives in the city of her birth. She will not leave Unug for Aratta in five years or ten. She has told me so herself. I, Enmerkar, have barley to fatten geese while you, Ensouggirana, through lack of rain do not. So it is I, Enmerkar, who will collect the goose eggs and goslings in baskets and cook them in my pots. The goose eggs and goslings will be eaten at a feast with the rest of the geese by the lords of Sumer, who do me the honour of submitting to me. They will all come to eat at my feast, happy to be my loyal guests a-plenty." Go now, messenger!'

'They will all come to eat at my feast'

The messenger left the city of Unug, took this message from Enmerkar up and down through the Zabu mountains and told it to Ensouggirana as he sat in his throne-room. The lord of Aratta summoned his advisers.

'What can I say? Enmerkar's bullish reply leaves me speechless.'

His advisers spoke.

'You were bullish yourself when you sent him a challenging message. Let it be. Don't say or do anything. Enmerkar will never submit to you.'

'Maybe he won't, but my city will be ruined and I will be a smithereen of pottery in its ruins before I submit to him!'

Wizardry

At this time, there was a wizard named Urgirnuna who had fled from the city of Hamazi when it was destroyed and now practised wizardry in Aratta. He spoke to the lord of Aratta's chancellor, Ansigaria.

'Why do the advisers tell the lord of Aratta to do nothing? The advice given in fierce Aratta has become feeble. I, Urgirnuna, know how to make the people of Unug dig more canals and submit to the Ezagina. When Unug submits, great armies can force submission from the north to the south of the Land and conquer from the forest mountain to the seashore. Unug will soon be filling cargo boats with its produce and ferrying them to the moorings outside the Ezagina in Aratta.'

Chancellor Ansigaria took the wizard Urgirnuna to speak with Ensouggirana. The lord of Aratta liked what the wizard said. He gave him five minas of silver and five minas of gold.

'If you make those people submit to me and serve me, you will have a place at my table with the finest food and drink. You will hold wealth and happiness in your hand.'

Urgirnuna left Aratta and went to Eresh, the city of ✳Nisaba, dingir of accounting. As he approached the cow-pens of Eresh the cows began to tremble with fear. He spoke to a cow as if it were human.

'You, cow! Who eats your cream? Who drinks your milk?'

6

'*Nisaba eats my cream,' replied the cow. '*Nisaba drinks my milk and the shining crown of my well-ripened cheese is served ceremonially in her great dining-hall. Until this has happened, *Nisaba, the oldest daughter of *Enlil, cannot complete her accounts.'

'Cows! Your cream will go to the tips of your glittering horns and stay there. Cows! Your milk will go to the tops of your buttocks and stay there!'

As soon as the wizard had said these words it happened. All the cream of the cows went to the tips of their glittering horns and stayed there. All their milk went to the tops of their buttocks and stayed there. The wizard then approached the sheep-pens and the goat-pens of Eresh. What had happened to the cows now happened to the sheep and to the goats. On that day the cow-pens, sheep-pens and goat-pens of *Nisaba fell silent. The only sound was the sad whimpering of hungry calves, lambs and kid-goats. It was a disaster. The cowherd was so shocked by what he saw he threw down his staff. The shepherd hung up his crook, weeping bitterly. The boy who tended the goats slipped away. There was no song from the singing milk-man. The cowherd and shepherd were the brothers Mashgula and Uredina. At dawn they went to the special place outside the Eresh city gate, knelt on the ground, raised their hands to the rising sun and reached out to *Utu.

'O *Utu, a wicked wizard came from Aratta and put a spell

on the animal-pens. He has stopped the flow of milk. The calves, lambs and kid-goats have nothing. There is no milk for us to drink and there will be no butter or cheese for us to eat. This wizard has brought misery and disaster.'

Ensouggirana submits to Enmerkar

✳Sagburu, the wise old woman, appeared outside Eresh. That ancient city was beloved by the dingir of the skies, ✳An, and the almighty dingir, ✳Enlil. They determined its destiny. On the bank of the River Euphrates, ✳Sagburu stopped the wicked wizard and challenged him. Five times they each threw a handful of fish spawn down into the river. From the first handful he conjured up a giant carp-fish. She conjured up an eagle, which caught the carp-fish, then flew off with it into the mountains. From the second handful he conjured up a ewe and a lamb. She conjured up a wolf, which caught the ewe and the lamb, then ran off with them into the desert. From the third handful he conjured up a cow and a calf. She conjured up a lion, which caught the cow and the calf, then ran off with them into the marshes. From the fourth handful he conjured up a long-horned mountain goat and a wild sheep. She conjured up a leopard, which caught the long-horned mountain goat and the wild sheep, then ran off with them into the mountains. From the fifth handful he conjured up a kid-gazelle. She conjured up a tiger and a lion, which caught the kid-gazelle, then ran off with it into the forest. The wizard's face clouded. He was deeply troubled. *Sagburu spoke to him.

'You used your wizardry wickedly. You dared to put a spell on Eresh, that ancient city beloved by *Ninlil, the mother of the moon dingir *Nannar-Suen. The destiny of Eresh is determined by *An and *Enlil. How could you do this?'

'I was foolish. Please don't be harsh with me. If you let me go I will declare your greatness in the mountains. I will sing your praises in Aratta.'

'No! You brought misery and disaster. You created a shortage of milk, butter and cheese. Because of you, the morning, midday and evening meals disappeared. There was nothing to put on the table in *Nisaba's great dining-hall. *Nannar-Suen, dingir of the moon, creates a non-stop flow of milk and you stopped it. For this you must die.'

*Sagburu picked up the wicked wizard from Hamazi who had acted for Aratta and threw him down into the river. She took away his life and life returned to the animal-pens of Eresh.

Life returned to the animal-pens of Eresh

9

When Ensouggirana was told about this he knew he was overpowered and sent a message to Enmerkar.

'You are truly *Inana's beloved chosen one. From east to west throughout the Land you are the great lord. I humbly submit to you. Ever since you were conceived you have been better than me. I am not your equal.'

Thus Ensouggirana withdrew his challenge to Enmerkar.

Praise be to *Nisaba, dingir of accounting!

Unug is bullish but lacks lapis lazuli

The city of Unug was bullish. From brick-built Kulaba, power pulsated throughout the Land, defeating disaster and determining destiny. The Eana was well established. It functioned smoothly and its supreme importance was acknowledged by all the lords of Sumer. At the heart of the House of the Skies was *Inana's special room, where her power shone out like silver in a rock. The city of Unug—with its floods of carp-fish and bountiful harvests of barley boosted by pleasant rains—flourished long before the trading island of Dilmun flourished. However, in those days there was no bathing, grooming and dressing in fine clothes for festivals because there was no trade. Nothing was exported and nothing was imported. No gold, silver, tin, copper, carnelian or lapis lazuli was brought from the mountains to Unug. The House of the Skies was not yet brightly coloured and its interior was not yet adorned with lapis lazuli. At this time Ensouggirana wore a crown of lordship for ✳Inana in Aratta but he was not equal to Enmerkar. Aratta had the House of Lapis Lazuli but nothing like ✳Inana's special room in the House of the Skies in Unug. ✳Inana's beloved chosen one whom she had called from the mountains was Enmerkar, the king of Unug. The day came when Enmerkar stood in ✳Inana's special room in the House of the Skies, raised his hands and reached out to his dingir.

Enmerkar tells ✳Inana his vision for the future
'O ✳Inana, I wish Aratta would carefully cut flawless lapis lazuli from the mountains and bring it to Unug. I wish this special room of your house in the Eana was adorned with lapis lazuli so that I—the radiant youth—could embrace you here. I wish Aratta would submit to Unug. I wish the people of Aratta would bring stone, timber, gold, silver, tin, copper, carnelian and lapis lazuli from the mountains. I wish they would build a magnificent house for you in Unug from where the wisdom of my kingship would flourish.

It would flourish like silver shining in a rock. It would flourish in the Apsu, that place whence flow the waters of the earth and the wisdoms of the world. In the Apsu I would sing a song of praise for you, then bring the wisdoms of ✳Enki

from Eridu to Unug. My kingship would be known and shown to all. The special crown of Unug would be placed upon my head in the great hall of your magnificent new house and sceptre-bearers would escort me to your special room. People would applaud and *Utu would shine upon me joyfully.'

*Inana's message

On hearing this, the jewel of *An, the Lady of the Mountains, the wise dingir, she who darkens her eyes for *Ama-ooshgumgalana, also known as *Dumuzid, spoke. She, *Inana, the Lady of All the Land, spoke to Enmerkar.

'Listen to me, Enmerkar, and do as I say. Choose from your men one who can speak well and run well. He will take my message. Take it where? Take it to whom? He will take my message up and down through the Zabu mountains. What is my message? It is this—Aratta must fulfil the wishes of Unug. The people of Aratta must bring stone, timber, gold, silver, tin, copper, carnelian and lapis lazuli from the mountains and build for me a magnificent house in Unug. From this house the wisdom of your kingship will

flourish. It will flourish like silver shining in a rock. It will flourish in the Apsu. You will sing a song of praise for me in that place whence flow the waters of the earth and the wisdoms of the world. Then you will take the wisdoms of ✳Enki from Eridu to Unug. Your kingship will be known and shown to all when the special crown of Unug is placed upon your head in the great hall of my magnificent new house and sceptre-bearers escort you to my special room.  People will applaud and ✳Utu will shine upon you joyfully. In the cool of the evening the people of Aratta, burdened by working all day in Unug, will gather in the Akalag meadows of ✳Dumuzid, which teem with ewes, lambs and kid-goats. Arise, Enmerkar, like the sunshine upon my bountiful bosom, for you are the jewel that sparkles at my throat. Praise be to you, Enmerkar, son of the sun dingir ✳Utu, lord of brick-built Kulaba, king of the city of Unug.'

Enmerkar sends ✳Inana's message to Aratta

Enmerkar heeded ✳Inana's words. He chose a man who could speak well and run well to be his messenger and told him to take ✳Inana's message up and down through the Zabu mountains.

'Messenger, say this to the lord of Aratta. "Here is what I will do to you, Ensouggirana. I will make your people flee like doves from a nest and Aratta will gather dust like any other devastated city. It will become a place cursed by ✳Enki and shrieked over by ✳Inana. Unless, that is, the people of Aratta fill leather sacks with gold, silver, tin, copper, carnelian and lapis lazuli. They must put the sacks on the backs of pack-asses and bring the pack-asses through the low mountain passes to Unug. Here the people of Aratta will build for ✳Inana a magnificent house, from where the wisdom of my kingship will flourish. The house will be built with the timber of boxwood trees, stretch out with colourful horns reaching up to the sun and have door-posts that gleam brightly." And messenger, sing to Ensouggirana the ✳Enki song. Do you remember the words? "That day will come when there will be no snakes, hyenas, scorpions, lions, wild dogs or wolves. People will have no predators and so no fear or trembling. On that day all people will speak to ✳Enlil with one voice, be they from Hamazi, twin-tongued Sumer and Akkad, or the Martu, who live in the wide open country. On that day the many tongues spoken by lords, princes and kings in their contests will become as one, thanks to ✳Enki, the dingir of wisdom and fresh water." Go now, messenger! By night push on like the south wind and at dawn be up with the dew.'

The messenger heeded the words of Enmerkar. He journeyed under the stars by night and under the sun by day. Where and to whom was he taking ✳Inana's message? He took it up and down the Zabu mountains. He journeyed over five, six, seven mountains and, looking up, saw the city of Aratta. He stepped joyfully into its courtyard and spoke proudly to Ensouggirana.

'My king sends you a fatherly message.'

'What does he say?'

14

'He says this. "Here is what I will do to you, Ensouggirana. I will make your people flee like doves from a nest and Aratta will gather dust like any other devastated city. It will become a place cursed by ✳Enki and shrieked over by ✳Inana. Unless, that is, the people of Aratta fill leather sacks with gold, silver, tin, copper, carnelian and lapis lazuli. They must put the sacks on the backs of pack-asses and bring the pack-asses through the low mountain passes to Unug. Here the people of Aratta will build for ✳Inana a magnificent house from where the wisdom of my kingship will flourish. The house will be built with the timber of boxwood trees, stretch out with colourful horns reaching up to the sun and have door-posts that gleam brightly." Now I will sing to you the ✳Enki song.'

The messenger sang the ✳Enki song to Ensouggirana.

The messenger sang the ✳Enki song

'However you reply, sir,' he went on, 'I will take your message to Unug. I will say whatever you tell me to say. I will speak your words to my master, who is the son of the sun dingir ✳Utu, the lord of brick-built Kulaba, the king of the city of Unug. He was conceived, carried, delivered and suckled by a mighty cow in the mountains. He grew from the soil of Aratta to be suited for the lordship of brick-built Kulaba. I will tell him what you say in the Eana.'

The lord of Aratta replied.

Ensouggirana rejects Enmerkar's proposal

'You must tell your master that I too am a special lord. ✳Inana, the captivating Lady of the Skies and dingir of much wisdom, has put me in Aratta among her wonders of the mountains to protect them. I am her broad gate that bars access to the mountains and her wonders. High and mighty Aratta cannot submit to lowly Unug. I cannot fulfil Enmerkar's wishes. I cannot meet his demands. I cannot accept his proposal.'

A message from ✳Inana cannot easily be rejected

Enmerkar's messenger listened to Ensouggirana's rejection. He had a reply. There was more to say.

'The great Queen of the Skies, she who rides the waves of powerful wisdom and graces the peaks of bright mountains, lives with my master and he is her servant. It is ✳Inana's wish that Aratta submits to Unug. She has spoken to Enmerkar. She told him this should happen. It must be.'

These words deeply troubled Ensouggirana. He stared at his feet with sad eyes trying to think of a reply. What should he say? What could he say? After a silence he suddenly bellowed like a bull.

Ensouggirana sets Enmerkar an impossible task

'Ah-ha! Tell this to your master, messenger. Tell Enmerkar that mountainous Aratta reaches high into the skies and deep into the mountains, with roots like a trap and branches like a net. Aratta may now be as weak as a sparrow because there is so little rain but it has the talons of the Anzud bird. It can make the blood of enemies flow down the ravines of *Inana's mountain barrier. The people of Aratta may be weeping with hunger but water is poured, flour is sprinkled and *Inana is respectfully celebrated. Your master is rushing to challenge me in the Zabu mountains with only five or ten soldiers from Unug. Well, if he is up for a contest so am I, as the saying goes, but I am up for a different kind of contest. To win a contest a man must know the strength of his challenger, just as a bull knows the strength of the bull beside him. Is your king up for such a contest or will he reject my challenge? Here are my words for you to say to Enmerkar, that lion who rests on his paws in the Eana. "My mountain city is like a warrior tall and fierce, with a face blood-streaked by

the rays of ✳Utu, going home at twilight. Aratta gleams with the moonlight sheen of majestic ✳Nannar-Suen high in the night sky and its darkly magnificent forests are impenetrable. This is Aratta, protector of ✳Inana's sky-high wonders in the mountains. If you, Enmerkar, rush here in a military attack, I will be the winner. You won't any more be filling sacks with barley, putting sacks on carts and ordering men to take the carts through the low mountain passes to the villages. If, however, you instead fill nets with barley, put the nets on the backs of pack-asses, with back-up pack-asses, and send the pack-asses through the low mountain passes to Aratta, then, when your barley is piled high in my courtyard, you will be the winner. Only thus can Aratta be cast aside by ✳Inana like a piece of rotten meat thrown to a scavenging dog, for ✳Inana is the glint in the pile of barley, the glow in the mountains, the lights in the villages, and the brightness of the city walls. She is the fiery angel for whom soldiers do their dance in battle. Barley in nets—only thus can Aratta submit to Unug." Repeat this whole message to me, messenger.'

The messenger repeated the whole message, then turned around like a frisky wild cow and flew off from Aratta like a sand-fly revelling in the cool, calm morning. He was joyful when he arrived back in Unug, hurried to the throne-room and told Enmerkar the message from Ensouggirana.

'Ah-ha!' he began, bellowing like a bull.

Enmerkar listened to the whole message then invited the messenger to sit beside him. He turned to the messenger and asked him his question.

'Does the lord of Aratta know what he's doing?'

Enmerkar sends barley in nets

The next day Enmerkar raised his head with the rising sun. He mixed water from the Euphrates with water from the Tigris, poured the water into two large jugs and placed them outside on the grass. Beside the two large jugs he placed two small jugs, which looked like their lambs. They stood before a golden statue made on a blissful day of ✳ Nanibgal, the young ✳Nisaba. Our Lady of the Clay Tablet and the Sharpened Reed, ✳Nisaba, dingir of accounting, opened her house of wisdom to Enmerkar and he knew what to do. He went to his lofty storehouse and took up his barley measure. He measured out some old barley and soaked it in water so it sprouted. He tightened the meshes on his nets and filled them with the sprouting barley. He added a measure of barley for the teeth of locusts, loaded the nets on the backs of pack-asses and added back-up pack-asses. Then he sent the pack-asses, the back-up pack-asses and their handlers off through the low mountain passes to Aratta. As he watched them go they looked from afar like a line of ants moving purposefully along a crack in the ground.

Enmerkar offers Ensouggirana a sceptre

Enmerkar summoned his messenger.

'Go across the Zabu mountains with a message for the lord of Aratta. Tell Ensouggirana I said this. "My kingly power rests in the base of my sceptre. The top of my sceptre symbolises the protection provided by brick-built Kulaba. Under the spreading branches of this protection *Inana refreshes herself in the Eana. You, the lord of Aratta, can have a small version of my sceptre if you will hold it in your hand like a string of carnelian and lapis lazuli beads when you carry it to me." Go now, messenger.'

Enmerkar's messenger set off for Aratta. He ran like a desert dragon, swift and unstoppable. As his feet pounded onwards the pebbles and grit of the high mountain paths leapt up into the air. When he entered Aratta its courtyard was crowded with people gazing at the pack-asses from Unug loaded with nets full of barley. There was enough barley to fill the Aratta storehouse and a measure for the teeth of locusts. The people of Aratta had a harvest as if from their own fields, made by the rain and the sun. Aratta's hunger was satisfied and the people were covering their fields with barley seeds. The advisers, however, were leaning against a wall wringing their hands.

'Aratta has been saved by the king of Unug but must our city now submit to him?'

As they placed their gold and silver in Ensouggirana's treasury, beside his damaged old sceptre, Enmerkar's messenger spoke to Ensouggirana.

'Hold it in your hand like a string
of carnelian and lapis lazuli beads'

'I bring you a fatherly message from Enmerkar.'

'What does he say?'

'He says his kingly power rests in the base of his sceptre. The
top of his sceptre symbolises the protection provided by brick-built
Kulaba. Under the spreading branches of this protection ✳Inana
refreshes herself in the Eana.'

'And?'

'And you, the lord of Aratta, can have a smaller version of this
sceptre.'

'Indeed?'

'Yes, if you hold it in your hand like a string of carnelian and lapis lazuli beads when you carry it to Enmerkar.'

After Ensouggirana heard these words he went to his bed-chamber, lay down without any food and didn't eat or sleep all night. When he got up in the morning he could only speak nonsense. Words went round and round in his mouth like barley munched by a donkey. What should he say? What could he say? After a long silence this is what he told the messenger to say to Enmerkar.

Ensouggirana sets Enmerkar a second impossible task

'Tell Enmerkar to put his mind and hand to making a sceptre with no wood, precious metal or gems. No ildag, simgig, cedar, cypress, hakur, palm, hardwood or zabalam. No poplar as used in chariot-making. No reed as used for whip handles. No gold, silver, tin, copper, carnelian or lapis lazuli. Only a sceptre so made will I hold in my hand like a string of carnelian and lapis lazuli beads. Only a sceptre so made will I carry to Enmerkar.'

Having heard these words, the messenger ran off like a braying donkey released from a chariot harness. He ran like a wild mountain donkey galloping over dry ground. He filled his mouth with mountain air as he hurried on, furiously, like a long-haired sheep pushing past others to get ahead. He set foot joyfully in brick-built Kulaba and repeated the message to Enmerkar.

'The only sceptre Ensouggirana will hold in his hand like a string of carnelian and lapis lazuli beads is a sceptre made without wood, precious metal or gems. No ildag, simgig, cedar, cypress, hakur, palm, hardwood or zabalam. No poplar as used in chariot-making. No reed as used for whip handles. And no gold, silver, tin, copper, carnelian or lapis lazuli. Only a sceptre so made will Ensouggirana carry to you.'

Enmerkar again achieves the impossible

Enmerkar knew how to meet this challenge thanks to *Enki, dingir of fresh water and wisdom. He ordered his steward to pound hairy hides with a pestle as if pounding herbs. The substance thus produced was poured into a hollow reed. The reed was placed first in sunlight then in shade, repeatedly, for five years. At the end of five years, Enmerkar split open the reed with an axe. Inside was the sceptre, hard and shiny. It looked splendid. Enmerkar anointed the sceptre with oil and put it into the hands of his messenger.

'Take this sceptre to the lord of Aratta.'

Holding the sceptre, the messenger ran to Aratta like a pelican gliding high among hill-tops, like a fly whizzing and buzzing above dust on the ground, like a carp-fish swimming and darting in deep water. He entered the courtyard of Aratta, gave the sceptre a little polish and presented it to Ensouggirana. The lord of Aratta was amazed and bedazzled by the sceptre, so successfully made without wood, precious metal or gems. In his bed-chamber, undone by fear, he spoke to his advisers.

Ensouggirana's last desperate ploy

'Aratta is undone. It is like a scattered flock of sheep. Its future is that of the crushed rebel land. *Inana has given high and mighty Aratta to lowly Unug. She is favouring the lord who sent her message over the Zabu mountains as clear as daylight. Where does this leave Aratta? How long must we submit? Will our hunger make us crawl to the lord of Kulaba? No!'

When Ensouggirana gave his reply to Enmerkar's messenger he spoke the words as solemnly as if they were written on a clay tablet.

'Enmerkar's champion must wrestle with my champion and this is how the contest will be determined. What's more, Enmerkar's champion must be wearing not black, white, brown, red, yellow or any combination of colours. Say this to Enmerkar.'

Having heard these words, Enmerkar's messenger set off swiftly from Aratta. Ulum-alam, ulum-alam, ulum-alam was the sound his feet made as they thudded through the Zabu mountains. Like a goat on the mountainside he looked towards Unug and like a big snake coming out of the fields he entered brick-built Kulaba. In the throne-room he told Enmerkar the message from Ensouggirana. When Enmerkar heard the message he was furious. He poured forth his reply in an angry flood.

Enmerkar writes the first letter

'Messenger, say this to Ensouggirana. "First, I will send you my champion wearing not black, white, brown, red, yellow or any combination of colours. My champion is ✳Enlil's favourite and will easily beat your champion. Second, you must stop prevaricating and act. You must let the people of Aratta walk in front of you like a flock of sheep and shepherd them to the lapis lazuli mountain. You must conquer the resistance of the mountain as if crushing a reed. Gold, silver, tin, copper, carnelian and lapis lazuli must be piled high in the courtyard of Aratta for transportation to the Eana in Unug. If you don't do this, Ensouggirana, I will make your people flee like doves from a nest and Aratta will gather dust like any other devastated city. It will become a place cursed by ✳Enki and shrieked over by ✳Inana." Messenger, sing again to Ensouggirana the ✳Enki song. "That day will come when there will be no snakes, hyenas, scorpions, lions, wild dogs or wolves. People will have no predators and so no fear or trembling. On that day all people will speak to ✳Enlil with one voice, be they from Hamazi, twin-tongued Sumer and Akkad, or the Martu, who live in the wide open country. On that day the many tongues spoken by lords, princes and kings in their contests will become as one, thanks to ✳Enki, the dingir of wisdom and fresh water." Can you remember these words?'

The messenger's mouth was so heavy he couldn't remember any words. Not one.

'I can't. There are too many words in the message.'

Enmerkar slowly patted a lump of wet clay until it became a smooth, flat tablet, then wrote the words of the message on the clay tablet. This had never been done before! It was done for the first time there and then! Enmerkar handed the written clay tablet to his messenger.

'Go now to Aratta. Give this to Ensouggirana.'

Carrying the clay tablet, the messenger set off from Unug like a bird flapping its wings in flight or a hungry wolf chasing a quick and nimble kid-goat. He journeyed over five, six, seven mountains and, looking up, saw Aratta. He entered its courtyard joyfully and presented himself to Ensouggirana.

'I bring you a fatherly message from my master, Enmerkar.'

'What does he say?'

'My king is a young ✳Enlil. His lordship and kingship are known to all.'

Enmerkar's messenger gave the written clay tablet to Ensouggirana.

'I am ready, sir,' he went on, 'to take your reply to my master. He is the son of ✳Utu, who was conceived, carried, delivered and

Enmerkar wrote the words of
the message on the clay tablet

suckled by a mighty cow in the mountains. He grew from the soil
of Aratta to become the lord of Kulaba and king of Unug. I will
give him your reply in the Eana.'

Ensouggirana can't read but Aratta is saved by ✳Ishkur

Ensouggirana looked at the clay tablet. The words of the message
had no voice. They were silent marks arranged in rows like soldiers

＊Iskur flashed and thundered in the cloudy sky

with their spears raised and daggers at the ready. The lord of Aratta frowned and his face clouded. He was deeply troubled. Was this his end? Must he submit? Suddenly, *Ishkur, the dingir of storms, flashed and thundered in the cloudy sky. He roared like a lion, shook the mountains and hurled heavy rain down on to the parched soil of Aratta. Chickpeas and barley sprouted and flourished. Barley was piled high in the courtyard of Aratta. Ensouggirana looked at the piles of barley in amazement. So did Enmerkar's messenger. The lord of Aratta spoke, happily.

'*Inana, the Lady of the Land, has not abandoned Aratta as her special place or given it up to favour Unug! She has not abandoned the Ezagina, her House of Lapis Lazuli in Aratta, and given it up to favour the Eana, her House of the Skies in Unug! She has not abandoned the shining wonders of the mountains and given them up to favour brick-built Kulaba! She has not abandoned her bejewelled bed and given it up to favour her flowery bed! She has not abandoned the lord of Aratta and given him up to favour the king of Unug! No! *Inana is favouring Aratta as rain splashes down all around us. The people of Aratta are *Dumuzid's chosen ones and well versed in the wise words of *Inana. When there was no rain we respectfully celebrated *Inana. Now, from her love for *Dumuzid, the dingir of shepherding, * Inana has sprinkled the water of life on our faces and the soil is serving us again!'

✳Inana appears in Aratta

At this moment Enmerkar's champion appeared in Aratta wearing not black, white, brown, red, yellow or any combination of colours, but a lion-skin. ✳Inana's song filled the air and so pleased her husband ✳Ama-ooshgumgalana that the words and music were perfection in ✳Dumuzid's ear. The wise old woman then appeared among the wonders of the mountains. As she approached she changed into a beautiful young woman looking and feeling her very best. Her eyes were darkened with lovely circles of black eye-liner painted all around them. Her spotless white gown was dazzling and the crown on her head sparkled like moonlight. With her was her beloved chosen one, Enmerkar, son of the sun dingir ✳Utu, lord of brick-built Kulaba, king of the city of Unug. She made Enmerkar sit beside her and for Aratta she made ewes and lambs multiply. For Aratta she made nanny-goats and kid-goats multiply. For Aratta she made cows and calves multiply. For Aratta she made jennies and foals multiply.

'Aratta shall have abundance,' ✳Inana proclaimed.

✳Inana spoke to Ensouggirana and he heard her song.

'It is the will of ✳Enlil that the contest between Aratta and Unug ends. Henceforth they must trade. The people of Aratta will mine gold, silver, tin, copper, carnelian and lapis lazuli. They will harvest figs and grapes. Their produce will be taken to Unug and piled high in the courtyard of the Eana.'

And so it was.

Aratta and Unug began to trade.

They both prospered.

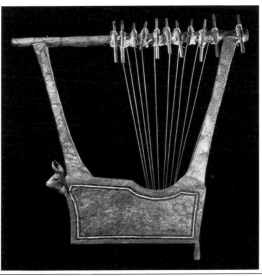

*Inana spoke to Ensouggirana and he heard her song

THREE KINGS OF WARKA

Lugalbanda

In this story Enmerkar has become an old king. There are seven proud princes of Unug and an eighth prince named Lugalbanda. In Sumerian 'lugal' means 'lord' and 'banda' means 'little'.

The city of Unug stood among fertile barley fields watered by the bountiful River Euphrates and the people of Unug, the black-haired people, were prosperous. They lived long, happy lives and every day brought gifts to their king, Enmerkar. They brought him mountain goats with pounding hooves and mountain stags with magnificent antlers. Over the hills and far away was that other city, Aratta. There was trade between Unug and Aratta but they were separated by the awesome Zabu mountains and the mysterious Lullubu mountains. Aratta was now a high and mighty city with artistry so fabulous it challenged the city of Unug. The day came when Enmerkar declared war on Aratta.

'I will take that proud place,' he said.

His herald sounded the call-up horn and when the men of Unug heard it every man turned to the man beside him. They arose all together like rooks arising from the best-seeded barley fields and rallied around their king. Enmerkar led his troops out of the city of

33

Unug past the barley fields and into the foothills of the mountains. They climbed the first hill like a flock of sheep and charged over the top like wild mountain bulls. They journeyed through the hills for five days. On the sixth day they rested and bathed. On the seventh day they entered the Zabu mountains and surged up the mountain paths like a stormy river. Riding that storm, on the crest of a wave, was their splendid king, Enmerkar, son of the sun dingir ✳Utu, lord of brick-built Kulaba, king of the city of Unug. Enmerkar's army had seven magnificent commanders, seven sons of Unug, seven proud princes raised at the table of ✳An, dingir of the skies. Each of the seven princes commanded many men, who each had many more men under his command. There was also an eighth prince whose name was Lugalbanda. His seven older brothers called him Princeling. He bathed with his brothers on the sixth day and on the seventh day entered the Zabu mountains with the Unug army. He was overawed by what he saw and stayed silent. When the Unug army was half-way to Aratta, Lugalbanda suddenly fell sick. His head hurt and his body jerked like a snake caught in a cleft stick. He lost his grip and his legs collapsed. He fell, bit the dust and lay on the ground like a trapped gazelle. The king couldn't help him and neither could his brothers.

'We must take Lugalbanda home to Unug,' said one.

'How can we?' said another.

Lugalbanda's teeth were chattering in the mountain cold. His

34

The day came when Enmerkar declared war on Aratta

brothers carried him to a nearby mountain cave and set about making it as cosy as a bird's nest. They laid out food and drink as if unloading a boat at harvest-time, but it looked like a funeral feast. They laid out hard-boiled eggs preserved in oil, all sorts of breads and cheeses, dates, date-syrup and sweetmeats suitable for a sick person. They filled water-skins with beer and wine and stacked them behind Lugalbanda's head. Above his head they hung a pot filled with hot aromatic oil. Beside his head they placed his bronze axe made of copper and tin mined in the Zubi mountains. On his chest they placed his dagger made of iron mined in the Black mountains. Lugalbanda's watery eyes were wide open and staring.

His lips were as hot as the noonday sun. His brothers lifted his head.

'There's no breath,' they murmured.

One of them spoke.

'If Lugalbanda arises from where he lies, *Utu may lead him through the mountains home to Unug. But if *Utu calls Lugalbanda to the land of the dead, when we return from Aratta we must come here to this mountain cave. We must collect his body and carry him home to Unug.'

Lugalbanda's brothers left him behind in the mountain cave like an old breeding bull left behind in the cow-pen. With their hearts full of sorrow and faces soaked with tears they marched on through the Zabu mountains towards Aratta, that high and mighty city with artistry so fabulous it challenged the city of Unug.

Lugalbanda does not die in the mountain cave

Lugalbanda lay sick in the mountain cave for three nights and three days. The evening of the third day was cool but Lugalbanda's whole body was sweating as if anointed with oil. He looked up at the setting sun, raised his hands and reached out to *Utu.

> 'O *Utu, let me be not sick while my brothers
>   carry on so brave,
> Still climbing in the Zabu mountains while
>   I'm stuck inside this cave.

It's so dismal here and dreary without the folks I know
    at home.
Without my mother, father, brothers, neighbours, I'm
    so utterly alone.
Everyone agrees a missing dog's a shock and sad,
But when a youth goes missing that's exceptionally bad.
I am in this mountain cave most unlikely to be found
And I'd hate to end my days here like a throw-stick on
    the ground.
Please don't let me die in these mountains as a weakling,
Belittled by my brothers who delight to call me
    Princeling.'

✳Utu heard Lugalbanda's words, beamed his blood-red rays into the mountain cave and let Lugalbanda live. ✳Inana, dingir of Unug, appeared in the sky as the bright evening star. Lugalbanda looked up, raised his hands and reached out to ✳Inana.

'O ✳Inana, how I miss my city! How I wish I was at
    home.
I wish this cave was Kulaba, the place where I was born.
A snake's domestic habitat on wasteland's to be found
And a scorpion is cosy in a crack which splits the ground.
I live in stone-dressed Unug where ✳Inana's house
    stands tall,
In that glorious, vibrant city where fine gents and ladies
    dwell.
I hear their calling voices into these mountains blowing
And I dread to die so far from home where cypress trees
    are growing.'

✳Inana heard Lugalbanda's words and beamed her twinkling rays into the cave. She covered Lugalbanda with compassion as if with a white woollen blanket. She let him sleep, like the sleeping sun dingir ✳Utu. ✳Nannar-Suen, dingir of the moon, appeared in the sky like a big white bull drinking the dark soup of the night. Lugalbanda awoke, looked up at the moon, raised his hands and reached out to ✳Nannar-Suen.

> 'O ✳Nannar-Suen, your majesty beams down from high above.
> Evil is something which you hate but justice fills your heart with love.
> A mighty poplar is your sceptre and chains restraining evil you pull tight.
> You also loosen many chains restraining what is right.
> Whenever you see evil you know what evil it can make.
> So you spit at evil with your poison like a hissing poisonous snake.'

✳Nannar-Suen heard Lugalbanda's words, beamed his silvery rays into the cave and gave Lugalbanda's legs the strength to stand. Lugalbanda stood up at last when the sun reappeared in the sky like a bright bronze shield brought from the treasury for young men to admire. Its golden rays brightened the cave and Lugalbanda looked up. He raised his hands and reached out to ✳Utu.

'O ✳Utu, when you're gone from us we humans close
   our eyes
And we know to wake and go about when you, ✳Utu,
   arise.
Without you no bird's netted and the missing slave stays
   free
But when two friends walk side by side you make their
   number three.
You are the friend, as well, of the one who walks alone
And your sunshine clothes the needy in a soft white
   woollen gown.
The elderly, both rich and poor, enjoy your shiny rays
And for the benefits you bring they utter endless praise.
Because of you wild bulls stay calm and furrows are well
   done,
So today I sing loud praises for you, ✳Utu, dingir of
   the sun!'

Lugalbanda runs, dreams and feasts with dingirs

Lugalbanda picked up his provisions. He picked up his dagger and
axe. He walked out of the mountain cave, heard life-giving water
flow and saw life-giving plants grow. Joyfully, he drank the water
and ate the plants, then ran through the Zabu
mountains like a galloping lone wild donkey all
day long. He was looking for his brothers and
when night fell he carried on looking for them
in the moonlight. His bright eyes saw nobody,

39

but then he stumbled on a circle of seven hot stones. His brothers had been here! Lugalbanda stopped. He put down his provisions. He put down his dagger and axe. He set about making a fire and it lit up the darkness like sunlight. He  had no oven and had never made bread but he had a fire and there was flour in the provisions left for him by his brothers. He mixed water into the flour to make dough then kneaded date-syrup into the dough to sweeten it. He put pieces of the sweetened dough on the hot stones around the fire. When his date-syrup cakes were baked he wrapped them in leaves plucked from a nearby tree. He was alone, so alone. A wild mountain bull who was calling to other wild mountain bulls came towards him. Lugalbanda stripped a long leaf so it was like a rope, then caught the wild bull and tied it to a nearby tree. Two funny-looking goats came by, a billy-goat and a nanny-goat. Lugalbanda caught the two funny-looking goats and tied them to the nearby tree. A vision of loveliness came towards him, swaying from side to side with a lapis lazuli flagon resting on her hip. It was ✳Ninkasi, dingir of beer. She filled Lugalbanda's cup, then disappeared. Lugalbanda drank the beer and began to feel sleepy. Sleep is all powerful. It can conquer kings. It creeps and seeps in like date-syrup then rises up like a hand or foot knocking down a brick wall. Lugalbanda lay on the ground and was soon deeply asleep. He came to the door of a dream and the door opened.

Two funny-looking goats came by

A dream is the closed tablet-casket of dingirs, the bed-chamber of ✳Inana. A dream can make you happy. A dream can make you sing. To a liar a dream tells lies. To a truthful person it tells the truth. ✳Zangara, the dingir of dreams, is the enhancer of humanity and the voice of what can be. He spoke to Lugalbanda.

'Who will take the tethered bull by the horns, wrestle it to the ground and slaughter it with his dagger and axe? Who will slit the throats of the goats so their blood soaks into the earth and the smell wafts to the wilderness where alert mountain snakes may sniff it? Who will pour cool water, beer and wine for a feast with dingirs?'

Lugalbanda woke up. He was alone in the mountains in the middle of the night. As if in a dream he took the tethered bull by the horns, wrestled it to the ground and slaughtered it with his dagger and axe. He slit the throats of the goats so their blood soaked into earth and the smell wafted to the wilderness where alert mountain snakes sniffed it. He poured cool water, beer and wine for a feast with the dingirs, then pulled out the livers of the goats and put them on the fire. The scented smoke arose—curling, whirling, swirling and drifting wispily up to the skies. The dingirs smelt the pungent aroma and appeared. ✳An, ✳Enlil, ✳Enki and ✳Ninhursanga all came to feast with Lugalbanda. Under the gaze of ✳Nannar-Suen, Lugalbanda placed his date-syrup cakes on a lapis lazuli table for ✳Inana. Her multi-coloured carnelian mountain stood in the mysterious Lullubu mountains. On top of her mountain was a tall, shaggy tree with long roots reaching down to rest like serpents in the seven-mouthed river of the sun dingir ✳Utu. In the branches of that tall, shaggy tree was the nest of the terrifying Anzud bird, who guarded the Lullubu mountains for the dingirs. Wild bulls fled from the Anzud bird to the foothills of the mountains. Wild stags fled from the Anzud bird to the peaks of the mountains. As ✳Utu reappeared, bringing in a new dawn, and the dingirs disappeared from Lugalbanda's feast, the Anzud bird opened his wings and let out a cry that cracked the ground in the Lullubu mountains. Then he flew up and away with his wife to go hunting for their food for today.

Lugalbanda has a plan

Lugalbanda was alone and lost in the mountains but he had a plan.

'If I can please the Anzud bird and his wife, he may help me find my brothers. He may help me find the Unug army and my way home to Unug.'

Lugalbanda set off towards the nest of the Anzud bird. It was made of bright twigs artfully intertwined. In the nest, alone, was a chick left behind while the Anzud bird and his wife went hunting. Lugalbanda crept into the nest and set about making a fuss of the chick. He darkened her eyes by painting beautiful circles of black eye-liner all around them. He

adorned her head with a pretty white sprig of sweet-scented cedar, above her head he hung a twist of salted beef, and into her mouth he popped his date-syrup cakes blessed by ✳Inana. Lugalbanda crept out of the nest and waited for the Anzud bird to come home from hunting. The Anzud bird appeared in the sky with a live bull dangling from his talons, a dead bull on his back, and a jet of bile spewing from his mouth. As he flew towards his nest he called to his chick. The chick did not reply. Always before when the Anzud bird called to his chick, she replied. The Anzud bird called to his chick again. The chick did not reply.

'What has happened to my chick?'

The Anzud bird let out a cry that reached up to the skies. His wife let out a cry that reached down to the Apsu. Their cries made mountain dingirs scurry like ants into cracks in the ground. The Anzud bird entered his nest and saw his chick. Her eyes were darkened with beautiful circles of black eye-liner painted all around them. Her head was adorned with a pretty white sprig of sweet-scented cedar and above her head hung a twist of salted beef. The Anzud bird was delighted.

'It looks as if a dingir lives here! If a dingir did this I will befriend him. If a man did this I will fix for him a fabulous fate!'

Full of fright and delight, Lugalbanda presented himself to the Anzud bird.

'O Anzud bird with sparkling eyes, how you frolic when you bathe in a pool. When you fly, your wings are as wide as a bird-catcher's net, your talons are hooks for dangling wild bulls, your chest is like ✳Nirah, the dingir of snakes, gliding through water, your back is as straight as a scribe's writing-stick, and your plumage is as plush as a luscious palm garden. O Anzud bird! You take my breath away!'

The Anzud bird looked at Lugalbanda. He liked him.

'Lugalbanda, you may go home with pride, like a boat at harvest-time loaded so high with cucumbers it casts a shadow.'

'Mmm….no!' said Lugalbanda.

He wanted more than that for himself and his heirs.

'Lugalbanda, you may go home with the power to slice your enemies like fish and pile them up like logs.'

'Mmm…no!' said Lugalbanda.

He wanted more than that for himself and his heirs.

'Lugalbanda, you may go home wearing the helmet of ✳Ninurta, as a hero fortified by the Anzud bird.'

'Mmm… no!' said Lugalbanda

He wanted more than that for himself and his heirs.

'Lugalbanda, you may go home carrying the milk-bucket of ✳Dumuzid overflowing with the fat of the land.'

'Mmm… no!' said Lugalbanda

He wanted more than that for himself and his heirs. He sounded like a kib bird skimming over a lake.

'Mmm… no! Mmm… no! Mmm… no! Mmm… no!'

The Anzud bird was exasperated.

'Lugalbanda! The braying ass and the straying ox must be brought into line and you must tell me what you want if I am to fix for you a fabulous fate.'

'I want to run. I want to run and run and run without ever tiring. I want to move like the sun in the sky, like the storm dingir *Ishkur, like *Inana as the bright evening star. I want to leap like a flame and flash like lightning. I want to go wherever I feel like going, set my foot wherever I cast my eye, reach wherever I wish to reach, loosen my shoes where my heart chooses. Then, when I'm back home in Unug, nobody will dare challenge me. They will let me be. They will respect me. I will have sculptors make breathtaking statues of you, the Anzud bird, to adorn the houses of dingirs and you will be admired throughout the land of Sumer.'

'Mmm… So be it. From now on, Lugalbanda, for you the roughest, toughest terrain will be like a smooth city street and when you are back home in Unug nobody will dare challenge you. You will have sculptors make breathtaking statues of me, the Anzud bird, to adorn the houses of dingirs and I will be admired throughout the land of Sumer.'

The Anzud bird flew up into the sky. Lugalbanda picked up his provisions. He picked up his dagger and axe. From above, the Anzud bird saw the Unug army in the distance. From below, Lugalbanda

'I will have breathtaking statues made of you, the Anzud bird'

saw the dust they kicked up spiralling into the skies. The Anzud bird flew back down and spoke to Lugalbanda one last time.

'Lugalbanda, beware. Good fortune has its own evil. Don't tell your brothers I have fixed for you a fabulous fate.'

The Anzud bird flew up and away.

He was gone.

Lugalbanda volunteers to take a message to *Inana.

Like a pelican emerging from the sacred reed-bed, like a dingir arising from the Apsu, like someone stepping from the skies down

47

to earth, Lugalbanda reappeared among his brothers.

'Princeling!' they shouted. 'It's you! We left you behind like a soldier fallen in battle because you weren't drinking milk or eating cheese. How did you find your way through these mountains? Nobody left behind here is ever seen again.'

They questioned Lugalbanda excitedly.

'The streams in these mountains are wide and their banks are steep. How did you cross them? How did you get drinking water from them?

'I stepped over the mountain streams, then lay on my side and drank from them as if from a water-skin. I prowled like a wolf and grazed in the meadows. I pecked at the ground like a wood pigeon and ate acorns.'

Lugalbanda's brothers listened to his story wide-eyed, then fussed around him like a flock of birds, hugging and kissing him. They brought him food and drink as if he were a chick in a nest, pleased he was alive and well. The next day the Unug army carried on through the Zabu mountains, marching in single file like a snake slithering through a pile of barley. On and on they went until they came to Aratta, that high and mighty city with artistry so fabulous it challenged the city of Unug. As soon as they camped outside Aratta's city wall, javelins rained down upon them. Sling-stones, as many as the raindrops that fall in a year, thudded on the ground all around them. This went on for hours and hours became days. Days became weeks and weeks became months. Months became a year. The barley in the nearby fields became golden. It was harvest-time and the men of Unug were worried. They wanted to go home to Unug but were afraid of monsters in the mountains. Their king, Enmerkar, was also worried. He wanted somebody to go through the mountains to Unug with a message for ✳Inana. He asked his commanders for a volunteer but nobody stepped forward. He asked his foot soldiers for a volunteer but nobody stepped forward. He asked his foreign fighters for a volunteer but nobody stepped forward. He asked his commanders, again, for a volunteer. Lugalbanda stepped forward.

'I will go but I must go alone.'

The king spoke to Lugalbanda.

'Will the sceptre of Unug be safe in your hands?'

'Will the sceptre of Unug be safe in my hands?'

'Yes. Will the sceptre of Unug be safe in your hands?'

'Yes. The sceptre of Unug will be safe in my hands.'

'Enter here.'

Enmerkar ushered Lugalbanda into his tent and told him the message.

'First, remind ✳Inana that when I was a young man she called me from the mountains to Unug. In those days Unug was full of marshes and there were water-reeds everywhere. Euphrates poplars grew where there is now dry land. ✳Enki showed me how to pull up the reeds, drain away the water and build. For fifty years I built. For fifty years I governed. When the wild Martu people—who have no fields of barley—rose up throughout the land of Sumer, there was a wall built by me to protect ✳Inana's city. But ✳Inana no longer loves me. She has abandoned me like the chick of the Anzud bird. I am stuck here with the Unug army outside the city of Aratta and she stays in her House of the Skies in Unug. I ask only that ✳Inana lets me go home to Unug. Then I will lay down my spear and she can break my shield. Tell this to my sister, ✳Inana.'

'I will,' said Lugalbanda.

When he walked from the king's tent his brothers were waiting outside. They barked at him as if he was a stray dog trying to join a pack of dogs but he strode on proudly like a lone wild donkey.

'Let another man go with you to Unug for the king,' they said.

'No, I will go alone. Nobody goes with me.'

Now he was telling them!

'Why go alone? If you don't have our dingirs with you we'll never see you again.'

Their hearts were pounding.

'The time has come. I'm going alone. Now.'

Their hearts sank.

Lugalbanda picked up his provisions, picked up his weapons and entered the Zabu mountains.

He ran and ran and ran without ever tiring. He moved like the sun in the sky, like the storm dingir *Ishkur, like *Inana as the bright evening star. He leapt like a flame and flashed like lightning. He went wherever he felt like going, set his foot wherever he cast his eye, reached wherever he wished to reach and loosened his shoes where his heart chose to. He ran over one, two, three, four, five, six, seven mountains. At the end of the day, that very same day, Lugalbanda entered the city of Unug just as food was being served for *Inana.

*Inana speaks to Lugalbanda

*Inana was sitting on her cushioned throne. Lugalbanda knelt before her. She looked at him as if he was her husband, *Dumuzid, and spoke to him as if he was her son, *Shara.

'Have you come alone, Lugalbanda?'

'Yes.'

'What is the message you bring from the mountains?'

'Enmerkar, son of the sun dingir *Utu, lord of brick-built Kulaba, king of the city of Unug, says you called him from the mountains long ago but you no longer love him. You abandoned him like the chick of the Anzud bird. He is stuck outside Aratta with the army while you stay in your House of the Skies in Unug. He asks only that he may come home to

51

Unug, then he will lay down his spear and you can break his shield.'

'Lugalbanda,' said *Inana, 'listen well to my words. In my waterskin a clear river flows, and beside the river is a water-meadow. In the water-meadow is a sacred pool and in the sacred pool are reeds. Swimming among the reeds are fishes—little fishes, big fishes and one very big fish who is the dingir of the fishes, with a silvery tail that swishes and flicks the reeds he swims among. Drinking from the sacred pool are the roots of tamarisk trees that grow around it. One of those tamarisk trees stands alone. Enmerkar must chop down that tamarisk tree and from it make a bucket. He must pull up the reeds in my sacred pool and with the bucket catch the very big fish who is the dingir of fishes, with a silvery tail that swishes and flicks the reeds he swims among. Enmerkar must cook that very big fish and serve it as an offering for success in battle, for battle is the game of *Inana. This is how Unug can challenge Aratta in the Apsu. Enmerkar must renew the city of Aratta and resettle its artists in the city of Unug. This is how Unug can acquire the fabulous artistry of Aratta.'

And so it was. That is what happened. Today, Aratta's battlements shine with sparkling lapis lazuli. Its walls and towers are built with clay bricks tinted bright red by tinstone mined in the mountains where cypress trees grow.

Praise be to Lugalbanda, the little lord who was called from the mountains by *Inana to become the new king of Unug.

'One very big fish who is the dingir of fishes, with a silvery
tail that swishes and flicks the reeds he swims among'

Gilgamesh

This story was originally written in Akkadian as well as Sumerian so some names have changed. Unug is Uruk. Anzud bird is Anzu bird. ✳An is ✳Anu. ✳Utu is ✳Shamash. ✳Enki is ✳Ea. ✳Ishkur is ✳Adad. ✳Inana is ✳Ishtar.

There was a king who plumbed the depths of human experience, got to the bottom of everything, understood mysteries and made known the unknown. He discovered what life was like before the great flood. He returned from a long, difficult journey exhausted but at peace and carved an account of his endeavours on a stone monument. He rebuilt Uruk's city wall and ✳Ishtar's House of the Skies. The upper part of the new city wall still shines like copper in sunlight. Its lower part is uniquely solid. Old stone steps lead up to the top of the wall and a walk along here provides fine views of ✳Ishtar's new house. The Eana has never been bettered since it was rebuilt. Its platform of kiln-fired bricks stands on foundations laid by the original seven sages. It occupies half a square mile of Uruk. The city buildings, the clay pits and the date groves each occupy a square mile. Uruk's wall surrounds a city of three and a half square miles. Hidden beneath the wall is a copper casket with a bronze lock. If the bronze lock is opened and the copper lid is lifted, the lapis lazuli tablet inside can be removed. Written on this tablet for everyone to read is the story of this king. It tells of all he endured and all he achieved. His name was Gilgamesh.

The most kingly of kings
Gilgamesh, king of Uruk, was the most kingly of kings. He was a hero with the energy of a rampaging wild bull, a leader of men who also shepherded them, a protective river bank and a flood wave smashing down stone walls. His father was *Lugalbanda, the king of Uruk who became a dingir. His mother was *Ninsun, the wild cow dingir. On his long and difficult journey he created new passes through mountains, dug wells on mountainsides and crossed oceans. He journeyed to the edge of the world in his quest to find the immortal *Utnapishtim-the-Far-Away and discover how to live forever. He rebuilt the dingir houses lost in the great flood and no other king could say 'I am king!' as he did. He was born to be famous. Two parts dingir and one part a man, he was very tall, very broad and perfectly proportioned. His rich black hair grew as thick as barley. He was the handsomest of men.

The young Gilgamesh strode around Uruk with his head held very high. He was like a proud wild bull. Nobody could challenge him. Nobody could match his aggression. He amused himself playing games with the young people and bullied them. He kept sons from fathers and daughters from mothers. He crushed the young men and abused the young women even if they were warriors' daughters or brides-to-be. Day after day and night after night Gilgamesh's behaviour worsened until people despairingly raised their hands to the skies and reached out to their dingirs, lamenting. The dingirs sympathised with the people and spoke to *Anu, dingir of the skies.

'Gilgamesh was born to be king,' they said, 'but the people of Uruk are suffering from his tyranny and lamenting. He takes young men from their fathers and crushes them. He takes young women from their mothers and abuses them, even if they are warriors' daughters or brides-to-be. Is this how a king should behave? Rampaging not shepherding? Do something, *Anu, please, before the skies are flooded with human tears!'

*Anu heard this plea and turned to *Mami, the creator of humans.

'*Mami, you created humans to do the work of little dingirs. Can you now create a doppelganger for Gilgamesh? Another hero? A man equal to Gilgamesh in strength and energy? Somebody who can balance him and bring peace to Uruk?'

*Mami wetted her hands and picked up a lump of wet clay. She moulded the clay with *Anu's words in mind. She placed the moulded clay far away in the wide open country and left it there.

Gilgamesh dreams

In Uruk, Gilgamesh was asleep in his palace. When he awoke he went to his mother, ✳Ninsun.

'I had a dream last night,' he said.

'Tell me,' said ✳Ninsun.

'I dreamed I was walking proudly with the young men of Uruk. The stars were shining brightly. One fell from the sky as a ball of rock and landed at my feet. I was attracted to it. I touched it. I tried to shift it but couldn't because it was too heavy. Others crowded around to admire it and kiss it as if it were a baby. They helped me lift it and I brought it to you.'

'This dream,' said ✳Ninsun, 'means your equal now exists. He lives in the wide open country. You will love him and bring him to me. I will treat him as your brother.'

'I also dreamed I saw a copper axe,' said Gilgamesh. 'It was lying on the ground in Uruk. Others jostled to see it. I picked it up. It looked strange but I loved it. I stroked it and held it close to me as if it were a woman. I strapped it to my side.'

'This dream,' said ✳Ninsun, 'means your friend is strong. He will be mighty in the Land and save you many times.'

'I am happy,' said Gilgamesh, 'that ✳Enlil has willed such a man to be my friend and guide me.'

Enkidu

In the wide open country a man as strong as ✳Ninurta the warrior was walking with the gazelles. Like them he wore no clothes. He had hair all over his naked body. The hair on his head was long and luxuriant, as thick as barley, like a woman's. He had no wife or children with him. No tribe or fellow citizens. The gazelles were his family and he grazed with them. When the gazelles were thirsty they went to a water-hole to drink alongside other animals. The wild man, Enkidu, went with them. One day, as Enkidu was kneeling in a water-hole to drink, he looked up and saw the hunter Shangashu watching him from behind a tree. Shangashu was shocked by what he saw. He stood still and silent until Enkidu and the gazelles had drunk their fill, then watched them walk away. The next day and the next Shangashu waited and watched at the water-hole, hidden nearby. Three times he saw Enkidu drink with the gazelles and other animals. Gloomy-faced and heavy-hearted he went home. He looked like a traveller at the end of a long and difficult journey.

'What happened?' asked his father.

'I have seen a wild man. He must be the mightiest in the Land. He's as strong as something from the skies. He roams the wide open country grazing with gazelles. At the water-hole I watched him drink with gazelles and other animals. I dared not approach him. He pulls up the traps I set and fills in the pits I dig so animals slip through my hands. He stops me catching anything and won't let me work as a hunter.'

'My son, in Uruk there's a man stronger than this wild man. Gilgamesh, too, is like something from the skies. Go to Uruk, present yourself to the king, tell him what you saw and he will tell you what to do. The wild man's strength can be overpowered by the special strength of a woman. Take with you to the water-hole a houri from the house of *Ishtar. When she shows off her body the wild man will go to her and his gazelles will leave him forever.'

The hunter Shangashu heeded these words. He went to Uruk and presented himself to the king. He told Gilgamesh what he had told his father.

'Take the houri Shamkat with you to the water-hole,' said Gilgamesh. 'When she shows off her body the wild man will go to her and his gazelles will leave him forever.'

The hunter went to the house of *Ishtar and found Shamkat. Together they walked to the water-hole in the wide open country. It was a three-day journey. When they reached the water-hole they waited another three days before they saw Enkidu.

'There he is!' whispered Shangashu to Shamkat. 'Show off your body. He will come to you and his gazelles will leave him forever.'

Shamkat let her clothes fall to the ground and showed off her body. Enkidu went to her. She took in his scent and he discovered the special power of a woman. With many lusty embraces he stayed with Shamkat for seven days and nights. When he was tired out, he tried to return to his family of gazelles, but they turned away

'When she shows off her body the wild man will go to her'

from him and ran off. He ran after them but his legs crumpled. His gazelles had left him forever. He had lost his natural self but gained self-awareness. He returned to Shamkat and sat at her feet. She gazed at him.

'You are so handsome, Enkidu, you are like a dingir. Why do you roam alone with animals in the wide open country? Let me take you to the walled city of Uruk. There you can visit the houses of *Ishtar and *Anu in the Eana. You can meet Gilgamesh, the king who lords it over the young people like a rampaging wild bull.'

Enkidu was pleased by Shamkat's words. He felt the need for a friend and she was friendly.

'Yes, Shamkat,' he said, 'take me to the houses of *Ishtar and *Anu. I will meet Gilgamesh. I will challenge him and change things in Uruk.'

'Yes, Enkidu, come to Uruk and let the people see you. In Uruk, the young men all wear sashes and there are festivals every day. Drummers beat out the rhythms, houris bring out their beauty for all to see, and old folk get out of bed to celebrate. But you, Enkidu, are not yet worldly-wise. You will meet Gilgamesh, a man  of both sorrow and joy. When you look into his face you will see his manly radiance and feel his powerful charisma. He is stronger than you and rarely rests. So don't challenge him, Enkidu. Gilgamesh is loved by *Shamash, *Anu, *Enlil and *Ea, who expanded his mind. He had a dream about you. He dreamed a heavy rock fell from the sky into Uruk. He picked it up and carried it to his mother, *Ninsun. He dreamed he found a copper axe on the ground. He picked it up, placed it at his side and took it to show *Ninsun. She told him his dream means a mighty man will come to be his friend and guide him.'

Enkidu was pleased by Shamkat's words and smiled. She picked up her clothes, put her cloak around Enkidu's shoulders and with the rest clothed herself. She took Enkidu by the hand with a dingir touch and led him to a nearby shepherds' hut. The shepherds stopped tending their sheep in the sheepfold and gathered around Enkidu, marvelling with curiosity.

'He is so like Gilgamesh!'

'He's shorter but bigger boned.'

'His body is built like a battlement wall.'

'He's Enkidu, with the strength of something from the skies.'

The shepherds took Enkidu and Shamkat into their hut, sat them down and offered them bread and beer. Enkidu was perplexed. He stared at the bread and beer. He didn't know what to do. He had never eaten bread. He had never drunk beer.

'He was suckled on the milk of wild beasts,' said one of the shepherds.

'He grazed with gazelles,' said another.

Shamkat spoke to Enkidu.

'Eat the bread, Enkidu. It's the food of human life. Drink the beer. It's a daily delight throughout the Land.'

Enkidu tasted the bread. It was delicious. He liked it so much he ate bread until he was full. He tasted the beer. It was delicious. He liked it so much he drank seven jarfuls. He became merry. His face glowed and he started to sing. The shepherds liked Enkidu's singing. They trimmed his beard, then combed and oiled his tangled hair. They gave him a tunic to wear and a weapon to carry. He put on the tunic and picked up the weapon. He looked like a warrior bridegroom. The day was ending and the older shepherds were falling asleep.

'I'll be your watchman tonight,' said Enkidu.

While the shepherds slept peacefully inside their hut, Enkidu stayed outside all night, protecting the sheep from predators. He fought off lions and killed a wolf. He was the best-ever strong man to keep watch. At dawn, a man looking worried hurried by carrying a bag of provisions.

'Call him over,' said Enkidu to Shamkat.

'Hey, mister!' she called.

The man stopped and came over.

'Where are you going in such a hurry?' asked Shamkat.

'I'm going to a wedding in Uruk, taking food in my bag for the feast.'

'What's wrong? Why are you worried?'

'At weddings in Uruk these days Gilgamesh has the bride and makes her pregnant before the groom can. This is Gilgamesh's birthright granted by ✳Anu.'

The words of the wedding guest angered Enkidu.

'I'm going to Uruk!' he said.

He led Shamkat from the shepherds' hut and they set off on the three-day journey to Uruk. When Enkidu entered the walled city, people crowded around. They marvelled with curiosity.

'He's so like Gilgamesh!'

'He's shorter but bigger boned.'

'He was born in the wide open country.'

'He was suckled on the milk of wild animals.'

'He grazed with gazelles.'

People jostled to be near Enkidu. Some young men kissed his feet as if he were a baby. They were happy to have a champion who could challenge Gilgamesh. Musicians were playing, animals were being slaughtered for the wedding feast, and the bride was waiting in the wedding house. Gilgamesh appeared. He looked like a dingir. Enkidu stood at the wedding house door. Gilgamesh approached, full of lust. Enkidu blocked the way with his foot. Enraged, Gilgamesh grabbed Enkidu. Infuriated, Enkidu grabbed Gilgamesh. Like two huge bulls they locked together in a wrestlers' embrace, testing each other's strength. Doors were smashed and walls were shaken as Gilgamesh and Enkidu fought in the streets of Uruk. Young men watched the fight with great excitement. In the end it was Gilgamesh who pinned down Enkidu, with the knee of one leg raised and his foot flat on the ground. His anger went. He relaxed his grip and turned away. Enkidu spoke.

'You, Gilgamesh, are... unique. *Ninsun, the wild cow dingir, gave birth to you as her son, you excel as a warrior and *Enlil destined you to be the king of Uruk. Me, I was born in the wide open country with hair all over my body, no tribe or fellow citizens, and no brother.'

'Why are you weeping?' asked Gilgamesh.

'Every fibre of my body aches.'

Gilgamesh took Enkidu's hand and they embraced as friends.

Gilgamesh decides to go to the forest mountain

Gigamesh and Enkidu stood on top of Uruk's city wall. They were watching a corpse float by in the river below. Gilgamesh spoke.

'No man can reach as high as the sky or as wide as the earth and no man can live beyond the days of his life but I, my friend, will make my name famous everywhere forever.'

'How, my friend?'

'I will do a deed never done before.'

'What will you do?'

'I will go to the forest mountain, chop down a magnificent tree and bring back sweet-scented timber for the city of Uruk.'

'Gilgamesh, this is a deed which must not be done.'

'Why not, my friend?'

'The forest mountain is the home of ✳Humbaba.'

'I will confront and maybe kill ✳Humbaba.'

'I will confront ✳Humbaba'

'You don't know ✳Humbaba, my friend. I do. When I roamed in the wide open country with gazelles I went to the forest mountain. It is huge. It is dark. It goes on for sixty leagues. No one ever ventures into the forest. If you take one step among its trees, ✳Humbaba hears you rustle, wherever you are and however quiet you are. His bellow is as loud as a raging, roaring flood. His speech sparks flames of fire. His breath is the breath of death. A fight with ✳Humbaba is unwinnable.'

'Enkidu, my friend, I will climb the slope of the forest mountain and chop down a magnificent tree. When it falls there will be a whirlwind.'

'My friend, ✳Humbaba is second only to the storm dingir ✳Adad in his ferocity. He guards the forest mountain for the almighty dingir ✳Enlil. He has seven auras of awesomeness. If you so much as put your foot on the forest floor you will be crippled. ✳Humbaba is not to be confronted. This is a deed which must not be done. This is a journey which must not begin.'

'My friend, why are you speaking like a weakling? Only dingirs live forever in the sky with ✳Shamash. A man's life is limited and whatever he achieves is no more than a puff of wind, but you and I together, Enkidu, will do a deed never done before. Are you afraid of being killed? Where's your bravery? I will go ahead. You can follow me saying "Be brave!", and even if I fall my name will be famous everywhere forever as Gilgamesh, the king who confronted

*Humbaba. You, Enkidu, were born in the wide open country. You have overpowered lions. Don't disappoint me now. First we will go to the forge. We will have new daggers and axes—the biggest and the best.'

'We will have new daggers and axes—the biggest and the best'

Getting ready to go

Gilgamesh and Enkidu went to the forge and spoke with the men who made daggers and axes.

'Blades of three talents each for the axes,' said Gilgamesh. 'Blades of two talents each for the daggers. Half a talent of gold each to decorate the handles of the daggers. We will have the biggest and the best.'

Then Gilgamesh summoned an assembly in the city square. He sat on his throne with Enkidu nearby and addressed the assembly.

'Elders of Uruk, I am going on a journey to the forest mountain. It is the home of ferocious ✳Humbaba, whose name is famous throughout the Land. In the forest mountain I will chop down a magnificent tree and when it falls there will be a whirlwind. I will bring back sweet-scented timber and my name will be famous everywhere forever as a fine son of Uruk. Young men of Uruk, you who like a fight, I am going on a journey to confront and maybe kill ✳Humbaba. I need your blessing for this journey so I will return home safely, walk through Uruk's main gate and see your faces again. What celebrations there will be when I return! We will have not one but two New Year festivals! The drumming will start and ✳Ninsun will be glad!'

Enkidu addressed the assembly.

'People of Uruk, I urge you to stop Gilgamesh going to the forest mountain. This is a journey which must not begin. This is a deed which must not be done. *Humbaba is not to be confronted. His shout is as loud as a raging, roaring flood. His speech sparks flames of fire. His breath is the breath of death. His forest goes on for sixty leagues and no one ever ventures among its trees. In ferocity, *Humbaba is second only to the storm dingir *Adad. Even dingirs don't challenge him. He was placed in the forest by the almighty dingir *Enlil to guard it with his seven auras of awesomeness. Whoever puts his foot on the forest floor becomes a cripple.'

One by one the people in the assembly spoke.

'Gilgamesh, your youthful bravery makes you reckless.'

'The deed you would do you don't understand.'

'*Humbaba's bellow is as loud as a raging, roaring flood.'

'His speech sparks flames of fire.'

'His breath is the breath of death.'

'His forest goes on for sixty leagues.'

'If you take just one step among its trees, *Humbaba hears you rustle.'

'He hears you wherever you are and however quiet you are.'

'In ferocity, *Humbaba is second only to the storm dingir *Adad.'

'Even dingirs don't challenge *Humbaba.'

'The almighty dingir *Enlil placed *Humbaba in the forest mountain.'

'To guard it with his seven auras of awesomeness.'

Gilgamesh smiled at Enkidu.

'I am not afraid of being killed,' he told the assembly.

The leader of the young men spoke.

'Gilgamesh, we want you to return safely to Uruk. We want to see our smiling king walk in through Uruk's main gate. Look long and hard before you strike a blow. Don't depend on your own strength alone. The one who goes ahead saves the other. The one who knows the way saves the other. Let Enkidu go ahead. Let him guide you. He knows the journey to the forest mountain. He is tried and tested in a fight. He will save you many times and bring you home to Uruk.'

The leader of the elders spoke.

'Enkidu, the assembly of Uruk will put our king into your hands. We urge you to bring him home safely and hand him back to us for his wives.'

Enkidu said nothing. Gilgamesh spoke.

'My friend, we will go to the sublime house of the wild cow dingir ✳Ninsun. My mother is a great, wise queen. She knows much and can assist us. I will seek her blessing for our journey.'

✳Ninsun adopts Enkidu as her son

Gilgamesh took Enkidu by the hand and they went to ✳Ninsun.

'Gracious ✳Ninsun,' said Gilgamesh, 'I will do a deed never done before. I will boldly begin a noble journey to the forest mountain. I will confront and maybe kill *Humbaba. In the forest mountain I will chop down a magnificent tree. When it falls there will be a whirlwind. I will bring back sweet-scented timber and my name will be famous everywhere forever as a  fine son of Uruk. I need your blessing for this journey so I will return home safely, walk through Uruk's main gate and see your face again. What celebrations there will be when I return! We will have not one but two New Year festivals! The drumming will start and you will be glad!'

*Ninsun listened to her son carefully then went to her private chamber. She bathed seven times in water sprinkled with juniper juice and petals from the soapwort flower. She dressed in a fitting gown fixed with a splendid pin and put on her crown. She walked up to her roof and lit incense. Its scented smoke arose. The pungent aroma drifted wispily up towards the sky. *Ninsun raised her hands and reached out to *Shamash.

'O *Shamash, my son who is so bullish will go far away and explore the distant unknown. He will go to the forest mountain, home of fierce *Humbaba. He will confront, challenge, fight and kill *Humbaba. He may not return. As Gilgamesh journeys, please protect him. Until he has killed evil *Humbaba, whom you hate, gaze upon him daily, all day. At twilight may your bride, *Aya, remind you to entrust Gilgamesh to the night-time's stars. Your ruddy glow,

✳Shamash, lights, shapes and moves all. While Gilgamesh journeys to the forest mountain, let the days be long and the nights be short. Let his stride be strong and his limbs be taut. Let him sleep well nightly as stars shine brightly thanks to your bride, ✳Lady Aya. When Gilgamesh finds ✳Humbaba, please release thirteen winds to assist him. North wind. South wind. East wind. West wind. Typhoons. Tempests. Hurricanes. Gales. Let them blow terrifying confusion to cripple and craze ✳Humbaba. Then Gilgamesh can strike with his weapons. Once this outburst of yours has assisted Gilgamesh, fleet-footed mules will take you to relax and revive with fellow dingirs. They will serve you dingir food and your brow will be bathed by your bride, ✳Lady Aya, with the fringe of her spotless white gown. O ✳Shamash, will my son Gilgamesh not one day sit among dingirs? Will he not one day be with you in the sky? Will he not one day wear his crown and carry his sceptre like ✳Nannar-Suen? Will he not one day become wise with the words of ✳Ea? Will he not one day dwell as a king in the world below? Only if he comes home safely from the forest mountain. Let it be so, ✳Shamash, I implore you.'

✳Ninsun extinguished the incense and walked down from her roof. She summoned Gilgamesh and Enkidu, then solemnly spoke these words.

'Enkidu, you came not from my womb into this world, but as the women in the house of ✳Ishtar adopt the foundling so I adopt you as my son.'

On to Enkidu's tunic ✻Ninsun fixed a splendid pin.

'For your journey to the forest mountain may the days be long and the nights be short. May your strides be strong and your limbs be taut. Make a camp every night to sleep deeply. Stop after twenty leagues to eat bread. Refill your water-skins whenever you can. Enkidu, will you guard Gilgamesh well on the journey to the forest mountain and back to the city of Uruk?'

'I will,' said Enkidu.

Departure

The day of departure dawned.

'Our journey begins today,' said Gilgamesh.

'This is a journey which must not begin,' said Enkidu.

'I can't show my bravery if I stay at home with you in Uruk! Take up your new dagger and axe, Enkidu. Take up your quiver and bow. We go now.'

Enkidu raised his hands and reached out to ✻Shamash for his blessing. Gilgamesh reached out to his very own dingir, ✻Lugalbanda. At the open main gate in Uruk's city wall, Gilgamesh spoke to the leader of the elders.

'I will be gone for many days journeying to the forest mountain, finding ferocious ✻Humbaba and killing that creature hated by ✻Shamash. While I am away you must protect the poor and weak, prevent the young men massing in the streets, and make sure the judges sit to settle disputes.'

The leader of the elders spoke to Enkidu.

'Enkidu, the assembly of Uruk now puts Gilgamesh into your hands. We need him to return safely and be handed back to us. Gilgamesh is our king.'

All the young men spoke to Gilgamesh at once.

'We want to see you return through this gate.'

'Look long and hard before you strike a blow.'

'Don't depend on your own strength alone.'

'The one who goes ahead saves the other.'

'The one who knows the way saves the other.'

'Let Enkidu go ahead and guide you.'

'He knows the journey to the forest mountain.'

'He is tried and tested in fighting.'

'He will save you many times.'

'He will bring you safely back to Uruk for your wives.'

Enkidu spoke to Gilgamesh.

'My friend, to begin this journey you must send these young men home and follow me. I have journeyed to the edge of the forest mountain and know the power of *Humbaba.'

Gilgamesh and Enkidu walked out through Uruk's main gate.

'May *Shamash assist in your success!' shouted the young men. 'May *Shamash be with you!'

Gilgamesh and Enkidu journey to the forest mountain

On their journey to the forest mountain, Gilgamesh and Enkidu travelled twenty leagues each day before they stopped to eat. They travelled another thirty leagues before they camped for the night. Travelling fifty leagues each day, they covered in three days the distance of a six-week journey.

At the end of every day, as *Shamash sank out of sight, Gilgamesh and Enkidu dug a well and refilled their empty water-skins. Gilgamesh climbed to find a place where he could sprinkle flour as a gift and ask the mountain for a dream. Enkidu made a shelter and inside it sprinkled a circle of flour. Gilgamesh entered the shelter, lay on the ground inside the circle and was soon deeply asleep. Enkidu lay on the ground at the shelter's entrance like a dropped net. Gusts of dust blew by outside. Five times during the journey Gilgamesh awoke in the middle of the night and cried out.

'Enkidu! What's happening? Did you touch me? Why do I feel so strange? Was a dingir nearby? I had an ominous dream.'

He sat with his chin on his knees and told his dream to Enkidu.

'We were travelling together and looked up at a huge mountain looming above us. It began falling and we were like two flies in a swamp.'

'This is a good dream,' said Enkidu. 'The mountain is *Humbaba and we will cast him down like a corpse on a battlefield.'

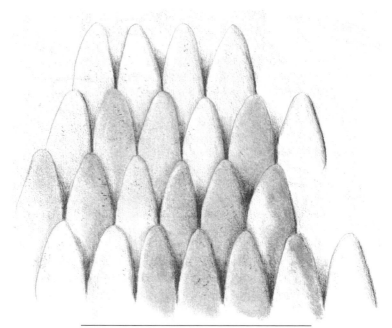

Gilgamesh had five ominous dreams on
his journey through the mountains

That night ended and ✳Shamash brought Gilgamesh and Enkidu
a new day for their journey. In his second dream Gilgamesh was
knocked to the ground by the falling mountain and his feet were
trapped beneath it.

'An extremely handsome young man appeared,' he told Enkidu,
'in a blaze of ever-brightening light. He grabbed me by my arms,

pulled me out of the mountain rocks and gave me water to drink from his water-skin. When I was calm he stood me on my feet.'

'This is a good dream,' said Enkidu. 'It means *Humbaba can knock you down but he can't kill you. The handsome young man in a blaze of brightening light is *Shamash, who will save you.'

That night ended and *Shamash brought Gilgamesh and Enkidu a new day for their journey. In his third dream Gilgamesh heard the sky shriek and the earth groan. At first it was dark and silent. Then lightning flashed and thunder cracked. Fire broke out. Flames flickered, flared and roared. Deadly blazing coals rained down. When the fire stopped burning the ground was strewn with hot embers.

'This is a good dream,' said Enkidu. 'It shows our fury in the fight with *Humbaba. We will be victorious.'

That night ended and *Shamash brought Gilgamesh and Enkidu a new day for their journey. In his fourth dream Gilgamesh saw a big black cloud in the sky. From this cloud the terrifying Anzu bird swooped towards him. It was hideous. It had the face of a lion and the talons of an eagle. It breathed out fire and Gilgamesh felt the heat on his face. A young man standing beside him seized the Anzu bird by its wings and threw it to the ground.

'Then I put my foot on it,' said Gilgamesh.

'This is a good dream,' said Enkidu. 'It shows we will capture *Humbaba and tie him up. The young man beside you in the dream is mighty *Shamash.'

That night ended and ✳Shamash brought Gilgamesh and Enkidu a new day for their journey. Gilgamesh's fifth and final dream on the journey to the forest mountain was more frightening than all four previous dreams.

'I dreamed,' he told Enkidu, 'I was holding the horns of a bellowing wild bull. It scraped and scarred the ground with its hoof, thrusting dark clouds of dust high into the sky. I was crouching in front of the bull, looking into its face. A man grabbed me from behind and pulled me away. He stroked my face and gave me water to drink from his water-skin.'

'This is a good dream,' said Enkidu. 'The wild bull is not an enemy. It is our protector ✳Shamash. He will take our hands when we are in peril. The man who gave you water to drink is your father and very own dingir, ✳Lugalbanda. This dream means we will do a deed never done before!'

That night ended and ✳Shamash brought Gilgamesh and Enkidu a new day for their journey. At last they saw the forest mountain.

✳Humbaba

The forest mountain was not far away. It was bigger than all the mountains they had climbed so far on their journey. It loomed high above them and they were like two flies in a swamp. The forest on the mountain was huge, dark and went on for sixty leagues.

Gilgamesh raised his hands and reached out to
✵Shamash with tears streaming down his face.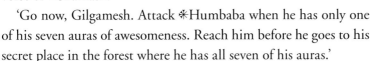

'O ✵Shamash, please assist me to be a fine
son of Uruk!'

He felt the heat from the sun and heard the
voice of ✵Shamash.

'Go now, Gilgamesh. Attack ✵Humbaba when he has only one
of his seven auras of awesomeness. Reach him before he goes to his
secret place in the forest where he has all seven of his auras.'

'Let's go!' said Gilgamesh.

They charged like wild bulls towards the forest mountain.

'Let's go back,' said Enkidu as they ran. 'This is a deed which
must not be done. ✵Humbaba is second only to the storm dingir
✵Adad in ferocity.'

'Let's go on. Why are you speaking like a weakling? We have
nearly completed our journey. Let's reach the seventh mountain. '

'You can go on but I must go back to the city. When I tell your
mother you're alive she'll be glad. If I then tell her you're dead she'll
weep bitterly.'

'Let's go on. Let's look for ✵Humbaba.'

'✵Humbaba's look is the look of death. If he shakes his head at
you you'll never go back to your city.'

'Let's go on. Don't disappoint me now!'

From within the forest came ✵Humbaba's terrifying bellow,

like a loud boom of thunder and a raging, roaring flood. Enkidu stopped.

'I can't go on. My legs won't move. My arms won't hold my axe.'

Gilgamesh took Enkidu's hand.

'You are tried and tested in fighting, Enkidu. You know to look long and hard before you strike a blow. You know the one who goes ahead saves the other. You and I together, Enkidu, will do a deed never done before and our names will be famous forever.'

They came to the edge of the forest and gazed up at the leafy branches of the trees—so many, so thick and so high above. On the forest floor they saw the well-trodden path among the trees made by *Humbaba when he climbed the slope of the forest mountain. This was a dingir place. Its coolness and shade were alluring and there was an abundance of sweet-scented timber. The leafy branches of the tree-tops rustled, then Gilgamesh and Enkidu heard the voice of *Humbaba speaking to them.

'Here they are, the clever pair—Gilgamesh and the wild man! You, Enkidu, you small-fry with no father, you squirt of tortoise spawn with no mother to offer you breast milk—I saw you often when you lived in the wide open country. I didn't kill and eat you then because you are too tiny a morsel to please my belly. And now, you treacherous wretch, you bring Gilgamesh to my forest and stand before me like a foreign foe. I can bite through Gilgamesh's wind-pipe, Enkidu. I can pull off his head and leave his headless dead body in a tree as a feast for the vultures and lions living in my forest...'

＊Humbaba's voice faded. The rustling in the trees ceased and there was total silence. Gilgamesh could not move. His toenails gripped the forest floor.

'Let's go back,' he said. '＊Humbaba is not to be confronted.'

'Let's go on,' said Enkidu. 'Why are you speaking like a weakling? Don't disappoint me now. We have already delayed too long. It is time to pour the copper into the mould. It is time to strike. Two strong cubs together can overpower a mighty lion.'

With their sharpened axes raised and their heavy daggers unsheathed, Gilgamesh and Enkidu entered the forest. They crept among the trees and boldly carried on until they came to the place where ＊Humbaba had all his seven auras of awesomeness. They heard a rustle in the tree-tops and then, again, the voice of ＊Humbaba speaking to them.

'O you, Gilgamesh, what a brave young man you are! You tall strong sapling! You raging wild bull chosen by the dingirs to be the king of Uruk! Your mother surely knew how to give birth to a son! Your wet nurse surely knew how to breast-feed! O Gilgamesh, touch the earth with both your hands, under the gaze of the sun dingir ＊Shamash.'

Gilgamesh touched the earth with both his hands, felt the hot touch of ＊Shamash on his back and spoke to ＊Humbaba.

'Would you like to be my kinsman, ✶Humbaba? You can have my big sister as your wife and my pretty little sister Peshtu as your concubine.'

'Yes, I would.'

'If you give up an aura we'll be kinsmen.'

✶Humbaba gave up one of his seven auras.

'Would you like cool water in a water-skin?'

'Yes, I would.'

'If you give up an aura we'll be kinsmen.'

✶Humbaba gave up another of his seven auras.

'Would you like flour fit for dingirs?'

'Yes, I would.'

'If you give up an aura we'll be kinsmen.'

✶Humbaba gave up the third of his seven auras.

'Would you like two big shoes for your two big feet?'

'Yes, I would.'

'If you give up an aura we'll be kinsmen.'

✶Humbaba gave up the fourth of his seven auras.

'Would you like two little shoes for your two little feet?'

'Yes, I would.'

'If you give up an aura we'll be kinsmen.'

✶Humbaba gave up the fifth of his seven auras.

'Would you like this piece of lapis lazuli?'

'Yes, I would.'

'If you give up an aura we'll be kinsmen.'

✳Humbaba gave up the sixth of his seven auras. He now had only one aura of awesomeness. ✳Shamash released thirteen winds to assist Gilgamesh. Winds from the north, winds from the south, winds from the east, winds from the west, all blew ferociously as typhoons, tempests, hurricanes and gales. They created terrifying confusion to cripple and craze ✳Humbaba. Mountains shook, white clouds became black and ✳Humbaba couldn't see through the swirling fog. He couldn't move forwards. He couldn't move backwards. When the whirlwind ceased and the fog disappeared, Gilgamesh saw ✳Humbaba standing in front of him. He was small and crippled with no aura of awesomeness. Gilgamesh stepped back as if to catch a snake. He leaned forward as if to kiss ✳Humbaba but, instead, punched him in the face. ✳Humbaba scowled and showed his teeth.

'You are a false hero!' he growled.

'Sit down,' said Gilgamesh.

'Sit down,' said Enkidu.

✳Humbaba sat on the forest floor and wept. Gilgamesh threw a rope over him as if he were a captured animal and tied his arms together at the elbows as a prisoner. ✳Humbaba grabbed Gilgamesh's hand.

'Let me go, please. I trusted you because you touched the earth with both your hands under the gaze of the sun dingir ✳Shamash.

In the name of ✻Shamash who led you here over the mountains, please let me go. The dingirs make me live in the forest mountain all alone guarding it for them with my seven auras of awesomeness. If you let me go I will show you the finest trees in the forest and you can take an abundance of sweet-scented timber to Uruk.'

From the bottom of his kingly heart, Gilgamesh pitied ✻Humbaba.

'Let the trapped bird fly free,' he said. 'Let the prisoner run home to his mother. Let ✻Humbaba become our porter and guide!'

Enkidu looked at Gilgamesh.

'O my friend, what a brave young man you are, you tall strong sapling, you raging wild bull chosen by the dingirs to be the king of Uruk. Your mother surely knew how to give birth to a son and your wet nurse surely knew how to breast-feed. But one so mighty, Gilgamesh, who is so trusting, will surely be devoured by destiny and never know what happened to him. Let the trapped bird fly free? Let the prisoner run home to his mother? Let ✻Humbaba become our porter and guide? We would never go back to our city!'

✻Humbaba looked at Enkidu.

'How can you speak like that to Gilgamesh? He is the king of Uruk and you run after him as his servant!'

These words so angered Enkidu that he raised his dagger and thrust it deep into ✻Humbaba's throat. Gilgamesh raised his axe.

'Finish it!' said Enkidu. 'Finish it before ✻Enlil stops it happening!

Do a deed never done before so our names will be famous forever!'
  Gilgamesh whacked down his heavy axe and chopped off
✻Humbaba's head. As he stuffed the severed head into a leather

Gilgamesh chopped off ✻Humbaba's head

bag, Enkidu tore out *Humbaba's bloody guts and threw them on the forest floor. Then they began hacking through the forest searching for the finest trees. Enkidu found a tree which was very fine indeed.

'With your strength, Gilgamesh, you brought down the forest guardian. Now you can bring down this very fine tree. Its leafy branches touching the sky will rest on the forest floor. It will become the sweet-scented timber of a great door in the Ekur. It will become a gift for the house of *Enlil. The River Euphrates will carry the timber to Nippur. *Enlil will like the door and be pleased with you.'

Gilgamesh chopped down the very fine tree. Enkidu lopped off its branches. They tied logs together to make a raft and carried the sweet-scented timber along the River Euphrates towards the ancient city of Nippur. Enkidu propelled the raft while Gilgamesh held the leather bag containing *Humbaba's head. In Nippur they entered the Ekur, the house of *Enlil. They knelt and kissed the ground. Gilgamesh tipped *Humbaba's head out of the leather bag as a gift for *Enlil. The almighty dingir looked at *Humbaba's head and spoke.

'Gilgamesh, did the dingirs determine that *Humbaba should be killed and his name be forgotten forever? No. You should have sat with *Humbaba and shared your food and water with him. You should have honoured *Humbaba as the terrifying creature who

Enkidu propelled the raft while Gilgamesh held
the leather bag containing ✳Humbaba's head

lived in the forest mountain guarding it for the dingirs with his
seven auras of awesomeness.'

✳Enlil gathered together the seven auras of awesomeness given
up by ✳Humbaba. The first aura he gave to the marshes. The
second aura he gave to the mountains. The third aura he gave to
the desert. The fourth aura he gave to the rivers. The fifth aura he
gave to the lions. The sixth aura he gave to the palace. ✳Humbaba's
seventh aura of awesomeness the almighty dingir ✳Enlil gave to the
dingir of prisoners.

The *Bull of Heaven

Back home in Uruk, Gilgamesh took off his head-band to wash his filthy hair. He let his hair fall down loose over his shoulders and back. He took off his soiled clothes and discarded them. He washed himself and his equipment. He dressed in a splendid new robe and on top of it put his best sash. He picked up his crown and placed it on his head. *Ishtar gazed upon him.

'Come to me, Gilgamesh,' she said. 'Come to me, my lover. Bring me your fruits. You shall be my husband and I shall be your wife. My gift to you is a lapis lazuli chariot with golden wheels and amber shafts, pulled by a team of lions and demon mules. Our house is filled with the fragrance of sweet-scented timber, greeting you as you enter. Let the finely wrought threshold kiss your feet. Inside, kings and princes, nobles and courtiers are kneeling to present to you their gifts from high and low throughout the Land. Now all your nanny-goats will bear triplets of kids. All the lambs from your ewes will be twins. Your loaded pack-asses will outpace all others and your horses will gallop in glory. No oxen will be better than yours at pulling the plough.'

'And what will I give you as my wife?' asked Gilgamesh. 'A head-dress? A gown? Food fit for a dingir and drink fit for a queen? You are a fire going out in the cold, a door letting in breezes, a palace consuming soldiers, an elephant throwing

90

off its cover, bitumen staining the cup-bearer's hand, a water-skin soaking its owner, mortar weakening a battlement wall, and a shoe which pinches the foot of its wearer. Who among your big, brave bridegrooms has thrived and survived to go up into the skies? The lover of your youth, ✳Dumuzi, was doomed to yearly death and lamentations. You loved the colourful allallu bird but slapped him and broke his wing. Now he stays in the woods crying "My wing… My wing… My wing…" You loved the lion, strongest of all, but dug for him pit after pit. You loved the horse, so trustworthy in battle, but decreed for him whips, spurs, and seven-league gallops with muddy water to quench his thirst, dooming his mother, ✳Silili, to perpetual sadness. You loved the shepherd who kept his embers alight so as to bring you cooked lamb every day. You slapped him and turned him into a wolf. Now the shepherd-boys hunt him down and his own dogs tear chunks of flesh from his thighs with their teeth. You loved your father's gardener, Ishullanu, who brought you a basket of dates every day to brighten your table. One day you looked at him and said, "Ishullanu, let us test your manliness. Touch me." Ishullanu said, "Me? Why me? My mother bakes bread for me and I have eaten. Do I want insults for my food and reeds to keep me warm at night? No." You slapped Ishullanu and turned him into a gnome standing still forever in his own garden. The pole of his shadoof goes up and down no more. His water bucket stays empty and dry. Is this to be my fate?'

When ✳Ishtar heard Gilgamesh's words she flew in a fury from Uruk up into the skies to see her father, ✳Anu, and her mother, ✳Antu.

'What happened?' they asked.

'Gilgamesh…' she sobbed. 'That wild bull rampaging in Uruk!'

'What did he do?

'He dishonoured me horribly.'

'Did you rebuke him?'

'I need the ✳Bull of Heaven to destroy him.'

'You can't have the ✳Bull of Heaven.'

'If you don't give me the ✳Bull of Heaven I'll smash down the door of the world below and release the dead. They'll outnumber the living and eat them.'

'The ✳Bull of Heaven lives in the night-time sky and grazes at the horizon where the sun rises. How can it exist on earth?'

'I will bring the sky to the earth with my scream.'

✳Ishtar let out a scream more terrifying than anything ever heard before or since. It covered both the sky and the earth like a blanket or a cloth.

✳Anu spoke.

'The ✳Bull of Heaven will bring seven years of famine to Uruk.'

✳Ishtar spoke.

'The widows of Uruk have already stored barley.'

'So be it,' said *Anu.

He put the *Bull of Heaven's tether into *Ishtar's hand. Like an ox-driver, *Ishtar pulled the *Bull of Heaven down from the sky to Uruk. Gilgamesh's minstrel, Lugalgabangal, picked up his lyre and in a song told his king what was happening.

'*Ishtar, with her dingir's pull,
Has brought from the sky to Uruk the *Bull
Which eats the grass till the soil is bare
And drinks from Engilua the water that's there.
Our double league canal now is dry but still
The *Bull from the sky hasn't drunk its fill.
It flattens our date-palms and has took
Into its mouth our harvest. Uruk
Is a city now filled with fear,
For the devastating *Bull of Heaven is here!'

'Sing your song, Lugalgabangal,' said Gilgamesh. 'Strum your strings. I'll drink another beer. Let my cup be filled!'

'Eat and drink, my lord,' said Lugalgabangal. 'Have no fear!'

Gilgamesh finished his beer then picked up his heavy dagger and axe. He spoke to his mother, *Ninsun, and his sister, Peshtu.

'Go to the house of *Ea,' he told them. 'Prepare to celebrate.'

'What will you do?' asked *Ninsun.

'I will kill the *Bull of Heaven, then give its meat to the orphans, its hide to the tanners and its horns to the house of *Ishtar.'

'The devastating ✳Bull of Heaven is here!'

Gilgamesh stepped outside the palace to confront the ✳Bull of Heaven. ✳Ishtar watched from the top of the city wall. The ✳Bull of Heaven bellowed. It snorted and a big pit appeared. A hundred young men fell into the pit and disappeared. The ✳Bull of Heaven snorted again and a second big pit appeared. Two hundred young men fell into the pit and disappeared. The ✳Bull of Heaven snorted a third time. A big pit appeared and Enkidu fell into it, up to his waist. With a mighty bound, Enkidu burst out of the pit and grabbed the ✳Bull of Heaven by its horns. It drenched him with a shower of its saliva and its thrashing tail splashed its dung everywhere.

'I have it!' shouted Enkidu. 'I have the *Bull of Heaven! I know its strength! Come on Gilgamesh! Your mother surely knew how to give birth to a son! Your wet nurse surely knew how to breast-feed! I'll go behind the *Bull of Heaven, grab its tail and put my foot on its back leg. You whack down your heavy axe between its horns. Hit its slaughter-spot. Hard!'

Enkidu went behind the *Bull of Heaven, grabbed its tail and put his foot on its back leg. Gilgamesh raised his heavy axe and whacked it down between the *Bull of Heaven's horns, hitting its slaughter-spot, hard. The *Bull of Heaven tossed its head from side to side then slowly collapsed. First it was like a huge lump of unshaped wet clay. Then it was like a flattened pile of barley.

'The *Bull of Heaven is slain!' shrieked *Ishtar.

Gilgamesh and Enkidu tore out the *Bull of Heaven's heart and fell to their knees. They held the heart aloft as a gift for *Shamash. *Ishtar bellowed.

'Gilgamesh, who dishonoured me horribly, has slain the *Bull of Heaven!'

With his dagger Gilgamesh hacked off the *Bull of Heaven's back leg and threw it up to *Ishtar. As it hit the city wall, *Ishtar jumped into the air and hovered like a frightened dove.

'The ✻Bull of Heaven is slain!' shrieked ✻Ishtar

'I'd drape its bloody guts around your neck if I could!' shouted
Enkidu.

✻Ishtar was surrounded by the women of her house. She stamped
her foot and they began a song of grief over the ✻Bull of Heaven's
back leg. Gilgamesh summoned his craftsmen to show them the
✻Bull of Heaven's horns.

96

'These horns are so big they need thirty minas of lapis lazuli each to decorate their brims,' said one craftsman.

'And two minas of gold each to sheathe their points,' said another.

'Between them they'll hold a kor of oil,' said another.

'The oil,' said Gilgamesh, 'will anoint the statue of my very own dingir, *Lugalbanda. The horns will hang in my bedchamber.'

Gilgamesh and Enkidu went to the River Euphrates and washed their hands. Hand in hand they strode along the main street of Uruk, surrounded by cheering crowds. They went to the palace for a party. To start the party Gilgamesh put a question to his serving-girls.

'Who is the best of men?'

'You are, Gilgamesh!'

The party went on all night until the revellers fell asleep.

Enkidu has ominous dreams

While everyone was asleep, Enkidu had an ominous dream. He dreamed he saw and heard dingirs discussing and deciding. *Anu, *Enlil, *Ea, and *Shamash were determining destiny.

*Anu spoke.

'They killed the *Bull of Heaven and *Humbaba, who guarded the forest mountain for us. One of them must die.'

'Let Enkidu die and Gilgamesh live,' said *Enlil.

97

*Shamash spoke angrily to *Enlil.

'Why must Enkidu die? You did nothing to stop them killing the *Bull of Heaven and *Humbaba!'

*Enlil spoke angrily to *Shamash.

'You stayed with them every day as their friend!'

Enkidu awoke from this dream and shook Gilgamesh.

'Wake up! I had an ominous dream.'

He told Gilgamesh his dream with tears streaming from his eyes and soaking his face.

'I will be taken from you, dear brother, over the threshold to sit with the dead. My eyes will never see you again!'

He sat up.

'But I see that door we gave to *Enlil. Better we gave it to *Shamash! That door was brought into being by me from a tree which knew nothing. I searched high and low, far and wide, to find the finest tree. We raised our axes and chopped down that tree. We transported it as sweet-scented timber to the house of *Enlil in the city of Nippur. We took it to the Ekur as a gift. Nippur craftsmen carved and carefully assembled that door. Every part of it was made from the same splendid timber. I did this good deed for what? How have I been rewarded? Better for me to raise my axe, disassemble that door and float it on a raft to Sippar, the city of *Shamash, whose winds assisted us in killing *Humbaba. Better to give that door to the house of *Shamash and with it a breathtaking statue of the Anzu bird. Now a king who lives after me can walk through that door, scratch out my name and write his own!'

Enkidu hurled these words at Gilgamesh.

'Enkidu,' said Gilgamesh tearfully, 'your lips are buzzing like flies! You know much but speak nonsense. Your dream is both awful and precious. It promises great grief for those left bereft. I will have a gold statue made of you. I will speak of you to *Anu, *Enlil, *Ea and *Shamash.'

Gilgamesh could not change the meaning of the ominous dream but when Enkidu heard the words of his friend he slept. Gilgamesh left the sick Enkidu sleeping deeply. Enkidu awoke at dawn when his face was lit by a beam of bright sunlight. He was alone, afraid and angry. He wept.

'O *Shamash, why me? Why must I be the loser and my friend be the winner? I curse that hunter who found me in the wide open country. May he be a loser for as long as he lives. May he fail at everything he does. May he never again catch a wild animal. May his traps be forever empty!'

When Enkidu cursed the hunter he remembered Shamkat.

'As for that houri from the house of *Ishtar, I curse her with an everlasting curse effective from this instant! Shamkat, your voluptuousness will vanish and men will choose younger, prettier houris. Your lovely purple lap will become forever filthy and you will be despised. You will have no alabaster powder or perfumed oil for your enhancement but only potter's clay to put on your face. Drunkards will vomit all over your finest dress. Drunkards and sober men alike will slap you about. You will have no child of your own to caress, no family home with silver, festive meals and other domestic delights. No builder will repair your house. You will walk through thorns which scratch your feet. You will stand in the shadows of the city wall. You will sit at the crossroads. You will sleep on a hard bench in a derelict building with screech-owls nesting in the roof. I curse you, Shamkat, because you lured me from the wide open country, where I lived happily and free with my family of gazelles. You weakened and defiled me!'

From the beam of bright sunlight, *Shamash spoke to Enkidu.

'Be not thus angry Enkidu! Shamkat tenderly found you, led you to human food, kingly drink, noble clothes. She led you to your friend and brother, handsome Gilgamesh. He will lay your body on a royal bed of honour. Kings in the land of no return will honour you. People in the city of Uruk will honour you with glorious lamentation. Gilgamesh will leave the city of Uruk. He will wander in the wide open country with his hair tangled and very long. He will dress only in the skins of the lions he overpowers.'

When Enkidu heard these words from *Shamash, his heart became calmer.

'May my curse upon Shamkat become a blessing. Shamkat, you

will be adored and desired by noblemen, kings and warriors. On their way to you they will shake out their hair and loosen their belts. They will give you earrings and brooches made of gold, silver, ivory, obsidian, carnelian and lapis lazuli. *Ishtar, the ablest of dingirs, will take you to a wealthy man with a full storehouse. For you he will forsake his wife and seven children.'

After Enkidu blessed Shamkat in his heart he slept deeply. He had a second ominous dream. When he awoke Gilgamesh was with him at his bedside.

'I had another ominous dream.'

'Tell me.'

Solemnly, Enkidu told Gilgamesh his second ominous dream.

'I dreamed I was standing between the sky and the earth as they parted with loud cracks of thunder. I saw a ghastly young man and was afraid. He had the face of the Anzu bird, the paws of a lion and the talons of an eagle. With terrific force he seized me by my hair. I hit him and he jumped into the air like a whipping top. He hit me and I sank to the ground like a capsized raft. Then he trampled all over me like a wild bull, crushing my body underfoot and drenching me with his poisonous saliva. "Save me, Gilgamesh!" I shouted. You didn't save me. The ghastly young man touched me and I turned into a dove with my wings trussed behind my back. He held me tightly and dragged me down to the world below. We took the way of no return to the land of the dead, where those who enter never leave. There is no light there and people exist in total darkness. They are clothed in feathers and eat clay and dust. Dust is everywhere—it covers the door and the bolt. When I entered this place, I saw the crowns of kings who ruled long ago. I saw the servants of *Anu and *Enlil, who set out bread, cooked meats and cool water in the houses of the dingirs. I saw the dingir servants who anoint the dingir statues and sing the dingir songs. I saw *Ereshkigal, queen of the world below. In front of her sat her scribe, *Belet-Seri, holding a clay tablet and reading aloud to her the names written there. *Ereshkigal looked at me. "Who brought this fellow here?" she asked.'

Enkidu dies

After Enkidu told this dream to Gilgamesh, he weakened. He stayed in bed day after day for twelve days. Every day Gilgamesh sat at the bedside of his dying friend. On the twelfth day Enkidu spoke.

'I will die in my bed, Gilgamesh, not in battle as a hero. Don't forget me, Gilgamesh. Remember me...'

'I will remember you, my friend, I will. You, Enkidu, were born in the wide open country and suckled by gazelles. Animals showed you the ways of the wild. The highlands and the lowlands will be bereft and grieve. The cypress, the cedar and the pine tree will be bereft and grieve. The hyena, the stag and the jackal will be bereft and grieve. The cowherd, the shepherd and the ploughman who

sings at his furrow will be bereft and grieve. The dairyman who
made the cheese you ate and the brewer who made the beer you
drank will be bereft and grieve. The wet nurse who butters babies'
bottoms and the houri who massaged you with perfumed oil will
be bereft and grieve. The old men of Uruk, who gave us their
blessing when we left for the forest mountain, will be bereft and
grieve. You will, old men, won't you? The young men of Uruk, who
watched us kill the *Bull of Heaven and celebrated our success,
will be bereft and grieve. You will, young men, won't you? And so
will I, Enkidu. I will lose the axe at my side, the shield at my chest
and my sash of honour. I will sob. I will sob like a wailing widow.
The River Euphrates itself will be bereft and grieve. How proudly
we walked along its banks! How happily we filled our water-skins
with its water! How furiously we fought *Humbaba in the forest
mountain. O Enkidu, how you ran like a hunted wild pony and
prowled like a panther… Enkidu, can you hear me?'

Enkidu was silent and still. His face was grey.

'What is this sleep which seizes you?'

Gilgamesh put his hand on Enkidu's chest. There was no
heartbeat. No breathing. He waited. Nothing. He covered Enkidu's
face with a veil. He circled around Enkidu like an eagle. He paced
up and down like a lioness whose cubs are trapped in a hunter's pit.
He tore out clumps of his thick black hair, ripped off his sash of
honour and tossed it aside in disgust. For days and nights he clung

to Enkidu's body, refusing to give it up for the funeral. Then he saw a maggot crawl from Enkidu's nostril.

Enkidu's funeral

'I will lay you on a bed of honour, Enkidu. Kings will kiss your feet. The pleasure-loving people of Uruk will be downcast. I will leave the city and roam in the wide open country wearing only lion-skins and with my hair unkempt.'

Gilgamesh summoned his craftsmen. Sculptors, coppersmiths, silversmiths, goldsmiths, wood-carvers, jewellers. Specialists in every art.

'You must make a statue of Enkidu better than anything ever made before.'

Gilgamesh broke the seal on the door of his treasury.

'Take this copper, silver and gold. Take lots and lots of gold. Use an iron rod for his backbone, alabaster and ivory for his limbs, obsidian for his eye-brows and eyes, lapis lazuli for his beard, carnelian for his cheeks, gold for his skin. He must have gold feet. Remember his quiver and bow.'

Cattle and sheep were slaughtered for the funeral feast. The great table made of elammaku timber from Lebanon was brought out. On it Gilgamesh placed two bowls. A carnelian bowl full of butter. A lapis lazuli bowl full of honey. He showed to *Shamash, one by one, the gifts to go with Enkidu for those he might meet in the land

 of the dead.

'Here is a baton carved from precious timber for *Ishtar, dingir of Uruk. May she welcome my friend and walk at his side. Here is a lapis lazuli flask for *Ereshkigal, queen of the world below. May she welcome my friend and walk at his side. Here is a carnelian flute for *Dumuzi, dingir of shepherding. May he welcome my friend and walk at his side. Here is a special chair for *Namtar, dingir of fate. May he welcome my friend and walk at his side. Here is a silver ring for *Qassutabat, the sweeper in the land of the dead. May he welcome my friend and walk at his side. Here is an alabaster plaque with an image of the forest mountain, inlaid with carnelian, for *Ninshuluhha, the cleaner in *Ereshkigal's house. May she welcome my friend and walk at his side. Here is a double-edged dagger, with a carving on its handle of the River Euphrates, for *Bibbu, the butcher in the land of the dead. May he welcome my friend and walk at his side. Let Enkidu not be sad in the land of no return.'

Gilgamesh leaves Uruk

When Enkidu's funeral ended, Gilgamesh left the city of Uruk.

'The fate of mortals has befallen Enkidu,' he said. 'My heart is full of grief and I fear death. The immortal *Utnapishtim-the-Far-Away, son of Ubara-Tutu, does not die. I will find him and discover how to live forever.'

Alone in the wide open country on a moonlit mountain pass, Gilgamesh saw lions in the distance and was afraid. He reached out to ✳Nannar-Suen, dingir of the moon.

'Enkidu has died. Now will I die? Please protect me, ✳Nannar-Suen.'

Gilgamesh slept and awoke in the moonlight, glad to be alive. When the lions came near and attacked him, he fought for his life.

The lions attacked and Gilgamesh fought for his life

He killed two lions, skinned them and ate their flesh. Dressed only in lion-skins he continued his quest to find the immortal *Utnapishtim-the-Far-Away and discover how to live forever. He dug new wells and quenched  his thirst with their water. He followed the breezes of the winds hither and thither. *Shamash was concerned about him. He bent down and spoke to Gilgamesh.

'Why are you roaming? You can never discover how to live forever, Gilgamesh.'

'If I must rest forever in the world below after my restless roaming, I will fill my eyes with sunlight now because the land of the dead is totally dark and a dead man never sees your radiance.'

Gilgamesh takes the night-time path of the sun

Gilgamesh came to the place in the Mashu mountains where *Shamash disappears out of sight at the end of each day. It was guarded by Scorpion People. Their auras of eerie twilight shrouded the mountains. As Gilgamesh approached the Scorpion People his face clouded with terror.

Scorpion Man spoke to Scorpion Woman.

'This may be a dingir,' he said.

'He's two parts dingir and one part a man,' said she.

'Who are you?' said Scorpion Man to Gilgamesh. 'Why are you

here in the Mashu mountains?'

'I am Gilgamesh, king of Uruk. I am searching for ✳Utnapishtim-the-Far-Away. He's a man who doesn't die. I must find him and discover how to live forever. I must enter this place in the Mashu mountains to continue my quest.'

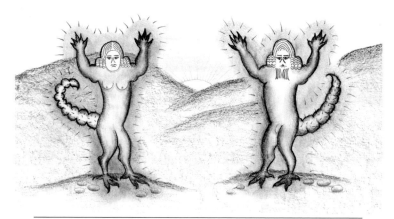

The Mashu mountains were guarded by Scorpion People

Only ✳Shamash enters here,' said Scorpion Man. 'You can't take the night-time path of the sun. That's never been done by any man.'

Scorpion Woman spoke to Scorpion Man.

'Gilgamesh is thin, weather-beaten and sad. Let him continue his search for ✳Utnapishtim-the-Far-Away.'

Scorpion Man spoke to Gilgamesh.

'If you take this path you must run in total darkness for twelve hours to reach the place where *Shamash arises to bring in a new dawn. Go quickly now, Gilgamesh, before *Shamash ends this day and enters here to take his night-time path!'

Gilgamesh heeded the words of Scorpion Man. He entered the night-time path of the sun, a tunnel of total darkness. Gilgamesh ran. He ran and ran non-stop for twelve hours. With the sun as a black hole rolling behind him, he felt its heat but saw no light. After twelve long hours Gilgamesh ran out of the darkness a moment before *Shamash rolled out behind him and arose to bring in a new dawn.

Gilgamesh meets *Siduri

By the pale dawn light Gilgamesh saw he was in a garden. The fruits of the trees glimmered and shimmered. They glinted and sparkled. These were dingir trees and lovely to behold. Bunches and clusters of luscious bright red carnelian droplets dangled from luminous rich blue lapis lazuli stems and branches. The leaves were glittering bright green gemstones. The cucumbers were smooth dark yellow gemstones. The dates were turquoise cowrie shells. Gilgamesh picked a carob pod. It was made of amber. He walked around the garden bedazzled and heard the distant ebb and flow of water lapping on the ocean shore.

This was the garden of *Siduri, the wise woman who kept a tavern at the edge of the world. Swathed in veils, *Siduri stood outside her house among her beer vats. As she lifted a golden lid, she saw Gilgamesh in her garden. He had a dingir look about him, but dressed only in lion-skins was a fright.

'He may be a killer,' said *Siduri to herself. 'For sure this man has captured and slaughtered wild bulls. Now he is walking towards my house!'

*Siduri hurried inside her house, closed and bolted the door, then ran up to the safety of her roof. Gilgamesh walked to her door, put his ear to it, heard nothing then shouted towards the roof.

'Tavern-keeper! Why have you bolted your door and run to your roof? Let me in or I will break in.'

'Who are you?'

'I am Gilgamesh, king of Uruk.'

'Gilgamesh?'

'Yes.'

*Siduri came down from her roof.

'Why are you so thin, weather-beaten and sad?' she asked

'I have journeyed far and wide through heat, cold and wind, wearing only lion-skins. My friend ran like a hunted wild pony and prowled like a panther. Together we climbed mountains and killed lions. We killed *Humbaba and the *Bull of Heaven. My friend Enkidu died. I waited and wept beside his body for days and nights, wanting and willing him to awake and be alive. When a maggot crawled from his nostril I was filled with fear. I am so afraid of death I journey far and wide remembering Enkidu's words. How can I be silent? Enkidu, whom I loved, turned into clay. Must I do so too one day? I am on a quest to find the immortal ✳Utnapishtim-the-Far-Away and discover how to live forever.'

'O Gilgamesh!' said ✳Siduri. 'You can't live forever. No human can. When the dingirs created humans to be their servants they gave them life but not life everlasting. The dingirs kept life everlasting for themselves! Enjoy your life, Gilgamesh. Keep yourself clean and dress well. Eat, drink and be merry. Care for the child who takes your hand and keep your wife always smiling in your manly embraces.'

'I can't live like that!' said Gilgamesh. 'Enkidu died and I am full of grief. I fear death. I must find the immortal ✳Utnapishtim-the-Far-Away and ask him how he lives forever. Do you know where he is?'

'I do.'

'You do?'

'✳Utnapishtim lives on the far side of the ocean.'

'I will go over the ocean.'

'Only ✳Shamash goes over the ocean. People can't.'

'Why not?'

'In the middle of the ocean, between here and the faraway shore, is the Sea of Death. If its water touches you, your life ends there and then. Urshanabi can pass through the Sea of Death only because the stone things he puts in his boat protect him from the deadly water.'

'Who is Urshanabi?'

'Urshanabi is *Utnapishtim's boat-man. Speak to him. He's in the forest beside the shore preparing to go over the ocean.'

Gilgamesh excitedly picked up his dagger and axe.

'I will go with him!'

'You may reach your destination or, if not, you can return, Gilgamesh. Go now!'

Gilgamesh meets the boat-man Urshanabi

Gilgamesh saw the forest beside the shore. It was not far away. He ran to the forest and entered it with his axe raised and his dagger unsheathed. Inside, the forest was dark and awesome. Overawed, Gilgamesh dropped like an arrow to the forest floor and let out a terrifying howl. Urshanabi saw the glint of Gilgamesh's axe and feared the worst. He tried to grab the axe but Gilgamesh hit him on the head. Urshanabi grabbed Gilgamesh's arm. Gilgamesh staggered around crazily. In his craziness he smashed the stone things to pieces, picked up the broken pieces and hurled them from the forest into the ocean.

Urshanabi looked at Gilgamesh.

'I am Urshanabi, boat-man of *Utnapishtim. Who are you?'

'I am Gilgamesh, king of Uruk. I came through the mountains on the path of total darkness taken by *Shamash before he arises to bring in a new dawn.'

'Why are you so thin, weather-beaten and sad?'

Gilgamesh told Urshanabi how he had journeyed far and wide wearing only lion-skins. He told him how Enkidu ran like a hunted wild pony and prowled like a panther. He told him how they climbed mountains together and killed lions. How they killed *Humbaba and the *Bull of Heaven. How Enkidu died. How he waited and wept beside Enkidu's body for days and nights, wanting and willing him to awake and be alive.

'When a maggot crawled from Enkidu's nostril I was filled with fear. I am so afraid of death I journey far and wide remembering Enkidu's words. How can I be silent? Enkidu whom I loved turned into clay. Must I do so too one day? I am on a quest to find the immortal *Utnapishtim-the-Far-Away. Can you take me over the ocean to the faraway shore?'

'You destroyed the stone things I put in my boat to protect me from the deadly water in the Sea of Death. Now we need three hundred very long poles. Take up your dagger and axe. Start making poles.'

Gilgamesh made three hundred very long poles. He and

Urshanabi put the poles into the boat, pushed off from the shore and began rowing over the ocean. As they rowed, the new moon became the full moon and then they rowed for three more days.

'Stop rowing,' said Urshanabi. 'Let the oars go. We are approaching the Sea of Death. If the deadly water touches you, your life ends then and there. Pick up a pole. Hold it high. Drop it deep into the deadly water. Don't let the water touch you. Let the pole go. Pick up another pole. Hold it high. Drop it deep into the deadly water. Don't let the water touch you. Let the pole go. Pick up another pole…'

Gilgamesh did this three hundred times. When the last pole was gone he held his hands wide apart so his lion-skins became a sail. The wind filled the sail and moved the boat.

'We have passed through the Sea of Death,' said Urshanabi.

'I see the faraway shore!' said Gilgamesh.

'We have passed through the Sea of Death'

Gilgamesh meets *Utnapishtim

On the faraway shore, *Utnapishtim-the-Far-Away was looking out over the ocean.

'Here comes Urshanabi,' he said to his wife.

The boat sailed nearer.

'There's a stranger in the boat with Urshanabi,' said *Utnapishtim.

The boat landed and Gilgamesh stepped ashore.

'I am Gilgamesh, king of Uruk.'

'I am *Utnapishtim. Or, as some say, *Utnapishtim-the-Far-Away. Why are you so thin, weather-beaten and sad, Gilgamesh?'

Gilgamesh told *Utnapishtim how he had journeyed far and wide wearing only lion-skins. He told him how Enkidu ran like a hunted wild pony and prowled like a panther. He told him how they climbed mountains together and killed lions. How they killed *Humbaba and the *Bull of Heaven. How Enkidu died. How he waited beside Enkidu's body for days and nights, wanting and willing him to awake and be alive. How he was filled with fear when a maggot crawled from Enkidu's nostril. How he was so afraid of death he journeyed far and wide remembering Enkidu's words.

'How can I be silent? Enkidu whom I loved turned into clay. Must I do so too one day? For an answer to this question I left my city of Uruk and set out to find you, the immortal *Utnapishtim, son of Ubara-Tutu. Every fibre in my body ached with grief. I didn't sleep on my journey and sleeplessness worsened my grief. I killed the wild animals I encountered—bears, hyenas, lions, leopards, tigers, gazelles, mountain goats. I ate most of their flesh, then scraped the rest off their skins so I could wear them. When I came to the tavern at the edge of the world my appearance frightened the tavern-keeper and she bolted her door to keep me out. Can I bolt a door and seal it with bitumen to keep out grief? Because of me there are no festivals and happiness has become wretchedness.'

✳Utnapishtim listened to Gilgamesh carefully, then said this.

'Why do you hang your head and prolong your grief, Gilgamesh? You have dingir flesh in you but you are human, so you will die one day as surely as the poorest and most ignorant man in Uruk. The difference between you and him is that you have a throne in the assembly of Uruk whereas he eats scraps, wears rags and puts on an old rope as a sash of honour. He has no advisers to guide him.'

Gilgamesh raised his head and ✳Utnapishtim continued.

'Why do the stars always shine in the night-time sky, Gilgamesh? Why does the sun arise every day to bring in a new dawn? Because the dingirs are ever wakeful and have been since the beginning of time. Yes, they took Enkidu from you, but you achieve nothing by keeping every fibre in your body aching with grief. You are only using up the days of your life as you approach the day of your death. All humans are mown down like reeds by death. The handsome lad and the pretty girl die young when death seizes them. No one sees the face of death. No one hears the voice of death. Death is relentless. People build houses and start families but then their legacy is disputed and divided. Sometimes there is war in the Land and many die. Sometimes the river floods and dragonflies float on the water. They look up at the sun momentarily and then their life is over. The dingirs decide the moment of death but don't disclose it until that moment comes.'

'What about you, *Utnapishtim?' asked Gilgamesh. 'You are different because you are immortal but you don't look different. In fact you are laid-back and your hands rest at ease. What makes you live forever? How is it that you will never die? Why is your life everlasting?'

'To tell you that, Gilgamesh, I must reveal dingir secrets.'

'I have journeyed far and wide for an answer. Tell me.'

'Tell you how I became immortal?'

'Yes.'

'I am immortal now but I was mortal before the great flood.'

'You lived before the great flood?'

'I lived before the great flood but not before the great drought and the great plague. They happened long before I was born as the mortal son of my mortal father, Ubara-Tutu, in the city of Shuruppak. Do you know Shuruppak?'

'I do. The ancient city of Shuruppak.'

'The great plague, the great drought and the great flood were sent to Shuruppak and the whole world by *Enlil to kill all the people.'

'Kill all the people?'

'The noise of raised human voices annoyed ✳Enlil. He decided to kill all the people so he could sleep. When ✳Enlil took the world on earth as his domain at the beginning of time there were no humans, there were only dingirs. ✳Mami created humans after the little dingirs turned against ✳Enlil and one of them was killed.'

'A little dingir was killed?'

'Yes. A little dingir was killed and dingir blood was kneaded into purified wet clay by ✳Ea, dingir of fresh water and wisdom. The dingir blood gave this clay a mind and a heartbeat. ✳Ea passed the clay to ✳Mami for her to create the first humans. She passed the clay around the assembly of dingirs for every dingir to spit on it.'

'Spit on it? Tell me the whole story.'

'The whole story?'

'Yes. Tell me what it was like at the beginning of time.'

'When there were no humans?'

'Yes. Tell me how humans came to be created.'

'And how they survived the great plague and the great drought?'

'Yes. The whole story.'

'And how I became immortal?'

'The whole story.'

'You have journeyed far and wide for an answer. I will tell you.'

✳Utnapishtim began.

*Utnapishtim tells Gilgamesh how and why humans were created

'In the beginning there were no humans, only dingirs. Three great dingirs divided the world into their domains. *Anu took the skies and went to live in the uppermost sky. *Enlil took the world on earth. He was the almighty dingir and leader of the dingirs. *Ea took the watery domain below the earth.'

'The Apsu…' said Gilgamesh.

'Yes. That place whence flow the waters of the earth and the wisdoms of the world. At this time, the great dingirs were served their bread and beer by little dingirs. To bake the bread and brew the beer the little dingirs grew barley. To grow barley they planted seeds and watered the fields. To water the fields they opened the River Euphrates, dug irrigation canals and dredged them to keep the water flowing. All this was hard work. The little dingirs worked hard all day long, digging and dredging, growing barley, baking bread and brewing beer day after day, for nearly four thousand years. They moaned and groaned. They mumbled and grumbled until…'

'Until what? What happened?'

'Until one day the little dingirs stopped working and cried out loud. "Enough! Let us go to the house of *Enlil and tell him he must free us from our work. It's too hard. We are ready to kill him!" The little dingirs made a blazing bonfire of their spades, picked up sharp sticks and set off for the house of ✳Enlil in the ancient city of Nippur. When they got to the Ekur it was the middle of the night and ✳Enlil was asleep. ✳Kalkal, the gate-keeper, bolted the gate and woke up ✳Nusku, the steward. ✳Nusku woke up his master. "What's that noise?" asked ✳Enlil. "Your house is surrounded by little dingirs," said ✳Nusku. "They are raising their voices against you." "Make ready your weapon, ✳Nusku," said ✳Enlil. "Stand by me." ✳Nusku made ready his weapon and stood by ✳Enlil. "Master," he said, "your face has gone pale. Are you afraid of the little dingirs? Send for ✳Anu and ✳Ea. Summon an assembly of all the great dingirs." ✳Anu came down from the uppermost sky. ✳Ea came up from the Apsu. All the great dingirs assembled in the Ekur. ✳Enlil spoke to the assembly. "My house is surrounded by little dingirs. They raise their voices against me. What is to be done?" ✳Anu spoke. "Send ✳Nusku to find out who is their leader." ✳Nusku went out and spoke to the little dingirs. "I come from the assembly of the great dingirs. Who is your leader?" "We have no leader," said the little dingirs. "We are all in this together. We have come to tell ✳Enlil he must free us from our work. It is too hard. We are ready to kill him." When ✳Enlil heard this, he wept and turned to ✳Anu. "I will show the little dingirs the power in the skies—one of them will be killed!" ✳Anu spoke. "Their work is very hard. We have heard them moaning and groaning, mumbling and grumbling for nearly four thousand years." ✳Ea spoke. "Let us ask our mother, *Mami. Maybe she can create something to do the work of the little dingirs." All the dingirs said "Yes!" *Mami spoke. "If *Ea gives me purified wet clay I will create human beings to do the work of the little dingirs." All the dingirs said "Yes!" *Ea spoke. "If a little dingir is killed I will knead dingir blood into the purified wet clay so it has a mind and a heartbeat. The killed dingir will be remembered forever." All the dingirs said "Yes! So be it!"

'Is that what happened?'

'Yes, and here's how it happened. On the first, the seventh and the fifteenth day of the month, wet clay was purified. One of the little dingirs was killed. *Ea kneaded dingir blood into the wet clay, one-two, one-two, one-two, so it had a mind and a heartbeat, one-two, one-two, one-two. The killed dingir would be remembered forever. *Ea gave the special clay to *Mami. She passed it around the assembly of dingirs. One by one they spat on it. *Mami spoke. "Now the humans soon to come into being will have a voice. They will do the work of the little dingirs." "Yes!" said all the dingirs joyfully as they rushed forward to kiss *Mami's feet. "We used to call you Mother of the Dingirs. Now we will call you Queen of the Dingirs!"

'So that's how *Mami became Queen of the Dingirs,' said Gilgamesh.

'And that's how humans got a voice,' said *Utnapishtim.

'What happened to the special clay?'

'✳Ea took the special clay that had a mind, a heartbeat and a voice into the chamber of destiny. Fourteen womb-dingirs were standing in two lines. ✳Ea held the pulsating clay, one-two, one-two, one-two, while ✳Mami sang her song. ✳Ea passed the clay to ✳Mami. She walked between the two lines of womb-dingirs handing out pieces of clay to her left and to her right. The domed birthing bricks were put in place. The womb-dingirs leaned forward, pressed down on the bricks and brought forth fourteen baby humans. Seven baby girls and seven baby boys.'

'These were the first humans?'

'Yes, the very first. Time passed and the baby humans became bigger. Breasts appeared on the chests of the girls and whiskers appeared on the chins of the boys. Walking in the city the boys and girls chose each other and married. The couples joyfully cried "✳Ishara!" and ✳Ishtar rejoiced. The wife made her home. The husband went out with his spade. He dug and dredged irrigation canals, grew barley, baked bread and brewed beer. After nine months the midwife put on her headscarf and belt, went to the home of the pregnant woman, opened her womb and brought forth a baby. The mother cut the umbilical cord.'

'And that's how people have multiplied ever since!'

✳Utnapishtim tells Gilgamesh how he survived the great flood

'People multiplied for nearly a thousand years,' said ✳Utnapishtim. 'They raised their voices. They talked, worked, fought, feasted and the noise of their raised voices annoyed the almighty dingir ✳Enlil. He summoned an assembly of dingirs and said this. "The people you created have multiplied. They raise their voices and the noise of their raised voices annoys me so I can't sleep. I will kill them all with a great plague." ✳Enlil sent ✳Namtar, dingir of fate, to kill all the people with a plague.'

'But some people must have survived. It can't be that all the people died. '

'Yes. Some survived.'

'How?'

'Beside the River Euphrates in the ancient city of Shuruppak lived a wise man with a mind, a heartbeat and a voice. He particularly respected ✳Ea, dingir of fresh water and wisdom. He reached out to ✳Ea and said this. "My people are being killed by a plague. What is to be done?" Then he heard the voice of ✳Ea.'

'He heard the voice of ✳Ea?'

'He did. ✳Ea said this to him. "Tell the people to respect only ✳Namtar, dingir of fate. They must build ✳Namtar a new house and present him with gifts. ✳Namtar will be touched and take away his hand. The plague will disappear." The wise man told this to his people and they began to respect only ✳Namtar. They built

✻Namtar a new house and presented him with gifts. ✻Namtar was touched and took away his hand.'

'Did the plague disappear?'

'It did. The plague disappeared and again the people multiplied for nearly a thousand years. They raised their voices. They talked, worked, fought, feasted and the noise of their raised voices annoyed the almighty dingir ✻Enlil. He summoned an assembly of dingirs and said this. "Again the people you created have multiplied. They raise their voices and the noise of their raised voices annoys me so I can't sleep. Now I will kill them all with a great drought." ✻Enlil sent ✻Adad, dingir of storms, to kill all the people with a drought. ✻Adad kept his rain inside the clouds and took the clouds away from the sky. The dark earth became white. Barley and vegetables died. People's faces were hollow with hunger. The daughter closed her door to her mother and parents ate their babies to survive.'

'Many died?'

'Many died.'

'But not all?'

'No. Not all. Beside the River Euphrates in the ancient city of Shuruppak lived a wise man with a mind, a heartbeat and a voice. He particularly respected ✻Ea, dingir of fresh water and wisdom. He reached out to ✻Ea and said this. "My people are being killed by a drought. What is to be done?" He listened but did not hear the voice of ✻Ea.'

'What did he do?'

'He took his bed to the river's edge and lay down to sleep. In a dream he heard a voice say this. "Tell your people to respect only *Adad, dingir of storms. They must build *Adad a new house and present him with gifts. *Adad will be touched and take away his hand. The drought will disappear." The wise man awoke from his dream and told his people what to do.'

'Did they do it?'

'They did.'

'Did the drought disappear?'

'It did, and yet again the people multiplied for nearly a thousand years. Yet again they raised their voices. They talked, worked, fought, feasted and the noise of their raised voices annoyed the almighty dingir *Enlil. He summoned an assembly of dingirs and said this, angrily. "Yet again the people you created have multiplied. They raise their voices and the noise of their raised voices annoys me so I can't sleep. I sent *Namtar to kill them all with a plague but some survived. I sent *Adad to kill them all with a drought but some survived. The secrets of the great dingirs have been revealed! Now I will send a flood to kill all the people and none will survive!" *Ea bit his lip. *Mami said nothing.'

'Was there a wise man living in Shuruppak?'

'There was. Me. I lived as the king of Shuruppak in a splendid reed house. One day I heard these words whispered through the reed wall of my house. "Reed wall, reed wall, hear what I say. Forget about your property and save your life. This house must be abandoned and a big round boat must be built. It must be covered with a roof so no rays of the sun come in. The boat must be filled with animals, birds, fish and the seeds of all things. It will be rained upon for seven days and seven nights." I asked this question. "What shall I tell my people?" Through the reed wall came this answer. "Tell your people that *Enlil and *Ea now disagree. Because you particularly respect *Ea you must leave *Enlil's domain and go to the Apsu." I told this to my people.'

'Did you build the boat?'

'I did. I abandoned my house and built a big round boat exactly as I was told to by the voice in the reed wall. I covered the boat with a roof so no rays of the sun came in. I gave the workmen beer and wine as if they were celebrating the New Year. They lowered the boat into the river. I took my gold and silver and filled the boat with animals, birds, fish and the seeds of all things. I went on board with my wife and children. They sat down to eat. I couldn't eat. I was vomiting. I couldn't sleep. I walked back and forth. When night came I shut the hatch on the roof of my boat.'

'Did the rain begin that night?'

'No. That night was quiet and calm. I didn't know what to expect. Then, as the night ended and *Shamash arose to bring in a new dawn, I saw a huge dark cloud on the horizon. Inside the cloud

✳Utnapishtim told Gilgamesh how he survived the Flood

✳Adad growled. The winds howled like wild donkeys. They bellowed like an angry wild bull. Everything went black. The blazing torches of ✳Adad's marching henchmen lit up the sky. ✳Adad attacked the land like a ferocious army and broke it to bits

127

like a smashed clay pot. The talons of the Anzu bird ripped open the clouds and rain fell non-stop for seven days and seven nights. The dingirs were terrified. They fled to ✳Anu in the uppermost sky and cowered there like dogs. ✳Mami, the Queen of the Dingirs, screamed like a woman in childbirth. Sweet-voiced ✳Mami was wailing. "How can ✳Enlil do this to the people I created?" she wailed. "They fill the ocean like fish spawn. They clog the rivers like drowned dragonflies. I hear them cry and I blame myself because I said nothing in the assembly of dingirs. When will my weeping cease? How can I live with this grief? My lips are parched. My throat is dry. I should be drinking beer but there are none to brew it and none to serve it." On the seventh day the rain stopped. I looked out of my boat.'

'What did you see?'

'I saw water everywhere. There was water all around my boat for as far as I could see. The water was flat and full of people who had become wet clay. I opened the hatch in the roof of my boat and the rays of the sun came in. I sat down and wept. My face was soaked with tears. I looked again at the water. My boat wasn't floating. It was stuck on top of Mount Nimush.'

'Mount Nimush?'

'It stayed stuck on top of Mount Nimush for another seven days and six nights surrounded by water. On the seventh day I released a dove. It found no branch to perch upon and returned. I released a

'My boat wasn't floating. It was
stuck on top of Mount Nimush'

swallow. It found no branch to perch upon and returned. I released
a raven. It didn't return. It had found a branch to perch upon,
nibbled a berry, lifted its tail and preened itself.'

'So the water was going down?'

'The water was going down and I could walk from my boat on to
dry land with my wife, children and animals. I breathed in the fresh
air and set about making a thanksgiving feast. I laid out fourteen

jars of burning incense. The scented smoke arose. It curled, swirled, whirled and drifted wispily up into the skies. The dingirs smelt the pungent aroma and appeared like a bright semi-circle of massive flies with their glittery wings a-flutter. *Mami spoke. "From now on I will always wear a sparkling lapis lazuli necklace as a reminder of this special moment. We dingirs will feed on the thanksgiving feast and *Enlil will not feed with us because he sent a great flood to kill all the people." But *Enlil saw the feast and flew to it in a fury. He spoke angrily to the dingirs at my feast. "How did these humans survive? It must be that *Ea has been revealing dingir secrets!" "No," said *Ea. "I did not reveal dingir secrets. A wise man discovered what to do in a dream and I whispered into a reed wall. From now on, *Enlil, when the people multiply and the noise of their raised voices annoys you so you can't sleep, you should send a lion, a wolf, or even a war to kill some of them but never again a great flood to kill them all!" "What does *Mami say?" said *Enlil. *Mami looked at *Ea and said this to the assembly of dingirs. "From now on, when people multiply, some women will never become pregnant, some women will die in childbirth, some women will give birth to dead babies, and some babies will be snatched from their mothers' laps by the wicked dingir *Lamashtu." After *Mami had spoken thus, *Enlil took my hand, took my wife's hand, touched our heads and spoke to us.'

'What did *Enlil say to you?'

'What *Enlil said to us was this. "Because you survived the great flood and saved the animals, birds, fish and seeds of all things, you will become like dingirs. You will live forever far away, where the rivers flow into the sea." So we did, so we do to this day, and so we will do, forever.'

'And that's how you became immortal?'

'Yes. That is how I became immortal and that is why some say my name as *Utnapishtim-the-Far-Away.'

Gilgamesh cannot live forever

'But what about you, Gilgamesh?' *Utnapishtim went on. 'Will you become immortal? For the dingirs to determine that you will live forever you must first live for seven days and seven nights without sleeping.'

'I can do that,' said Gilgamesh.

He sat with his chin on his knees and immediately fell asleep.

'Look at him,' said *Utnapishtim to his wife. 'He wants to live forever!'

'Wake him up,' said *Utnapishtim's wife. 'He must return to Uruk.'

'He deceives himself and others. Make him bread for each day he sleeps as proof of the truth and put a mark for each day on the wall.'

Every day Gilgamesh slept, *Utnapishtim's wife made bread for him and put a mark on the wall. On the seventh day *Utnapishtim shook Gilgamesh and he awoke to the smell of freshly baked bread.

'I slept for only a moment,' he said.

'No you didn't,' said *Utnapishtim. 'You slept for seven days and seven nights. Here's the bread baked for you today. Here's the bread baked for you yesterday. Here's the bread baked for you the day before yesterday. Here's the bread baked for you three days ago. Here's the bread baked for you four days ago. Here's the bread baked for you five days ago. Here's the bread baked for you six days ago. And here's the bread baked for you when you fell asleep seven days ago. Look, each day is marked on the wall.'

Gilgamesh saw the seven breads baked day by day. He saw the seven stages of decay.

'Today's bread is fresh,' said *Utnapishtim. 'Yesterday's is less fresh. The bread baked the day before yesterday is going stale. The bread baked three days ago is stale. The bread baked four days ago is stale and going mouldy. The bread baked five days ago is very stale and mouldy. The bread baked six days ago is very stale and very mouldy. The bread baked seven days ago is so stale and so mouldy it's uneatable.'

'Everything decays and death awaits me,' said Gilgamesh.

*Utnapishtim turned to his boat-man Urshanabi.

'You can go now, Urshanabi. You need never return. Take with you this man you brought here, after you show him where to wash himself and throw away his lion-skins.'

'Here's a new set of kingly clothes, Gilgamesh,' said
✳Utnapishtim's wife. 'They are new and will stay fresh throughout
your journey home.'

Urshanabi took Gilgamesh to the washing place. Gilgamesh
washed, put on his new clothes and threw his lion-skins into

'Here's a new set of kingly clothes, Gilgamesh'

the ocean. He and Urshanabi boarded the boat to depart. ✻Utnapishtim's wife spoke to her husband.

'Will you give Gilgamesh a parting gift?'

'Yes, I will. Gilgamesh, you can't live forever but on your journey home you can find a prickly plant at the bottom of the ocean which will make you young again.'

Gilgamesh finds the prickly heartbeat plant, and loses it

On the journey home Gilgamesh tied stones to his feet, went over the side of Urshanabi's boat and plunged through the water to the bottom of the ocean. There, in the depths, he found the prickly heartbeat plant. Its thorns scratched his hand but he seized it tightly. He cut the stones from his feet, hurtled up through the water and splashed out into the air. He climbed back over the side of Urshanabi's boat. They were now on the other side of the ocean, near the shore not far from the city of Uruk.

'This is the heartbeat plant,' said Gilgamesh to Urshanabi. 'It can make you young again. In Uruk I will give some to an old man. If he becomes young again after he eats it I will eat some myself.'

They landed the boat, left it on the shore and began walking to Uruk. At thirty leagues they stopped to eat. They walked another thirty leagues then camped for the night. Nearby was a cool pool. Gilgamesh went into the pool to bathe. He left the heartbeat plant beside the pool with his kingly clothes. The scent of the heartbeat plant attracted a snake. She slithered close, ate all the heartbeat plant then slithered away, made young again. She left behind her old skin. When Gilgamesh saw what had happened he wept.

'The prize for my blood, sweat and tears has been snatched from me, Urshanabi, by this slippery lion slithering along the ground. I will never find another heartbeat plant because I don't know where to dive for it. We abandoned your boat by the shore and have come too far to go back.'

'The prize for my blood, sweat and tears has been snatched from me by this slippery lion slithering along the ground'

The city of Uruk

The next day they saw the city wall of Uruk. Its upper part shone like copper in the sunlight. Its lower part was uniquely solid.

'This is my city,' said Gilgamesh.

They climbed the old stone steps and walked along the top of the city wall.

'Look, Urshanabi, there is ✳Ishtar's new House of the Skies. The Eana has never been bettered since it was rebuilt. Its platform of kiln-fired bricks stands on foundations laid by the original seven sages. It occupies half a square mile of Uruk. The city buildings, the clay pits and the date groves each occupy a square mile. Uruk's wall surrounds a city of three and a half square miles.'

Take a last look at this lapis lazuli tablet...

Take a last look at this lapis lazuli tablet, reader. Put it back in the copper casket. Lower the lid of the casket and close the bronze lock. Replace the casket under Uruk's city wall.

This was the story of Gilgamesh, all he endured and all he achieved. He was the most kingly of kings, two parts dingir and one part a man.

✳Inana and Warka

List of Illustrations & Photographs

The visual clues to the story world of the *Three Kings of Warka* are mostly photographs of, or illustrations based on, objects displayed in the Mesopotamia public galleries of the British Museum (BM). All the illustrations are by Eleanor Allitt unless otherwise indicated. All the photographs are courtesy of the Trustees of the British Museum unless otherwise indicated.

Front cover
Illustration of ✻Ishtar by Sadiq Toma, based on a cylinder seal in the Oriental Institute, University of Chicago

Page 2, recurring
Illustration of stones symbolising mountains, based on a narrative frieze in BM Room 10B, Ref. WA 124904-5

Page 3, recurring
Illustration of ✻Inana's rosette symbolising fertility and abundance, based on (i) a plaque, BM Room 56, Case 2, Ref. ME 126397A, (ii) image on the end of the Uruk Trough, BM Room 56, in a case on its own, on the wall beside the door into Room 57, Ref. ME 120000

Page 4, recurring
Illustration of Sun symbol (✻Utu/✻Shamash), based on the symbol being pointed at by the king in the alabaster stele of King Ashurnasipal in the Great Court of the BM, Ref. ANE 118805

Page 5
Illustration of feast, based on the Standard of Ur—Peace Side, BM Room 56, Case 17, Ref. ME 121201

Page 9

Photograph of dairy scene—modern cast of Sumerian ware, BM Room 56, Case 6, Ref. ME 116754; original in the Iraq Museum, Baghdad

Page 10, recurring

Illustration of Moon symbol (✻Nannar-Suen), based on the symbol being pointed at by the king in the alabaster stele of King Ashurnasipal in the Great Court of the BM, Ref. ANE 118805

Page 15

Illustration of ✻Enki by Jennifer Iles, based on (i) a greenstone cylinder seal, the third one down in the display in Room 56, Case 11, Ref. ME 89115 and (ii) the enlarged photograph of the impression made by this cylinder seal, in an information wall poster near Case 5

Page 21

Photograph of jewellery, BM Room 56, Case 15, items (6) and (8) Refs. ME 121424 and ME 121421

Page 27

Photograph of diplomatic letter tablet from Ishkun-Dagan, BM Room 56, Case 11, Ref. ME 121205

Page 28

Illustration of ✻Ishkur based on a wall panel showing soldiers carrying away on thrones a row of gods captured from a defeated enemy. The storm god ✻Ishkur/✻Adad is at the back of the row, holding a fork of lightning. BM Room 8, Ref. WA 118931 & 118934

Page 31

Photograph of the Silver Lyre, BM Room 56, Case 19/20, Ref. ME 121199

Page 34
Photograph of the Standard of Ur—War Side, BM Room 56,
Case 17, Ref. ME 121201

Page 40
Photograph of Ram-in-the-Thicket, BM Room 56, Case 17,
Ref. ME 122200

Page 46
Illustration of the Anzud Bird, based on Imdugud—Anzud Bird, BM
Room 56, above doorway into Room 57, Ref. ME 114308

Page 52
Illustration of fisherman, based on a fragment of narrative frieze on
the wall which also displays a large narrative frieze showing a stone
winged bull being moved to Nineveh, BM Room 9, Ref. WA 102072

Page 59
Photograph of statue of female nude, BM Room 55, Case 13,
Ref. ME 124963

Page 65
Photograph of ✳Humbaba, BM Room 56, Case 22, Ref. ME 116624

Page 67
Photograph of dagger, BM Room 56, Case 18, Ref. ME 122701
Photograph of replica alloy axe with gold binding, BM Room 56,
Case 15, Ref. ME 120689

Page 76
Illustration of stones symbolising mountains, based on a narrative
frieze in BM Room 10B, Ref. WA 124904-5

Page 85
Illustration of severed head, based on wall panel, BM Room 9,
Ref. WA 124786-7

Page 87

Illustration of men on raft, based on an image high in one of the large wall panels showing a stone winged bull being moved to Nineveh, BM Room 9, Ref. ANE 124822

Page 92

Illustration of bull, based on wall panel showing the capture of Babylonians by Assyrians, BM Room 9, Ref. WA 132814

Page 94

Photograph of bronze amulet of *Ishtar, BM Room 55, Case 13, Ref. ME 119437

Page 104

Illustration of king killing lion, based on wall panel, BM Room 10A, Ref. WA 124874-7

Page 106

Illustration of Scorpion People, based on (i) images on large pot, BM Room 55, Case 5, Ref. ME 91941, (ii) boundary stone, BM Room 55, Case 1, Ref. ME 90858

Page 112

Photograph of model boat, BM Room 56, Case 11, Ref. ME 133043

Page 125

Photograph of Flood tablet: the 11th tablet of the *Epic of Gilgamesh*, BM Room 55, Case 8, Ref. ME K 3375

Page 127

Photograph of the peak identified as Mount Nimush in the Zagros mountains overlooking the Sahrizor valley in Iraqi Kurdistan, taken by Dr Karen Radner in September 2011

Page 131

Illustration of new kingly clothes, based on images on a glazed terracotta tile, BM Room 55, Case 11, Ref. ME 90859

Page 133
Photograph of pottery fragment showing a snake with flickering tongue, BM Room 56, Case 1, Ref. ME 127617

Page 135 and back cover
Illustration of ✳Inana's eyes overlooking Unug by Ed Coyne, based on a Jemet Nasr period cylinder seal in the Iraq Museum, Baghdad

Glossary

*Adad—the Akkadian name for *Ishkur, dingir of storms

Akkad—the land to the north of Sumer

*Ama-ooshgumgalana—another name for *Dumuzid, dingir of shepherding

Ansigaria—Ensouggirana's Chancellor

*An—dingir of the skies

*Anu—Akkadian name for *An, dingir of the skies, father of *Ishtar

*Antu—*Ishtar's mother and consort of *Anu

Anzu(d) bird—eagle with the head of a lion, guardian of the Zabu Mountains

Apsu—underground fresh-water domain, home of *Enki/*Ea

Aratta—city east of Sumer, rival of Unug/Uruk, rich with raw materials

*Aya—bride of *Shamash

*Belet-Seri—*Ereshkigal's scribe

*Bibbu—butcher in the Land of the Dead

*Bull of Heaven—embodiment of the constellation of Taurus

Dilmun—ancient trading centre on the island now known as Bahrain

*Dumuzi—Akkadian name for *Dumuzid, dingir of shepherding

*Dumuzid—Sumerian name for the dingir of shepherding

*Ea—Akkadian name for *Enki, dingir of wisdom and fresh water

Eana—*Inana's/*Ishtar's House of the Skies in Unug/Uruk

Ekur—house of *Enlil in Nippur

Enlil—dingir of the Earth and leader of the dingirs

Enki—dingir of wisdom and fresh water

Enkidu—wild man created by *Mami to be Gilgamesh's equal

Enmerkar—king of Unug

Ensouggirana—lord of Aratta

Eresh—Sumerian city, home of *Nisaba, dingir of accounting

Ereshkigal—dingir of the Land of the Dead in the world below

Eridu—city south of Sumer, home of *Enki/*Ea

Euphrates—westernmost river flowing south through Mesopotamia

Ezagina—*Inana's House of Lapis Lazuli in Aratta

Gilgamesh—king of Unug/Uruk, son of *Lugalbanda and *Ninsun

Hamazi—city located in the land now known as Iran, original home of the wizard Urgirnuna

Humbaba—guardian of the forest mountain, protected with seven auras of awesomeness

Inana—dingir of Unug

Ishara—another name for *Ishtar

Ishkur—dingir of storms

Ishtar—Akkadian name for *Inana

Ishullanu—*Anu's gardener, turned into a gnome by *Ishtar

Kalkal—gate keeper of the Ekur, house of *Enlil

Kulaba—centre of royal power in Unug/Uruk

Lamashtu—female dingir who attacks pregnant women and babies

Lugalbanda—eighth prince of Unug who becomes king of Uruk

✳**Lugalbanda**—Lugalbanda-turned-dingir, father of Gilgamesh

Lugalgabangal—Gilgamesh's minstrel

✳**Mami**—queen of the dingirs and the creator of humans

Martu—nomad people

Mashgula—cowherd brother of Uredina

Mashu mountains—where the sun rises and sets, night-time path of the sun

Mina—unit of weight measurement, about half a kilogram

Mount Nimush—mountain where ✳Utnapishtim's boat landed after the great flood

✳**Namtar**—dingir of fate

✳**Nannar-Suen**—dingir of the moon

✳**Nanibgal**—name of the young ✳Nisaba, dingir of accounting

✳**Nisaba**—dingir of accounting

✳**Ninshuluhha**—cleaner of ✳Ereshkigal's house

✳**Ninhursanga**—a dingir of birth and motherhood

✳**Ninkasi**—dingir of beer

✳**Ninlil**—✳Enlil's bride

✳**Ninurta**—warrior dingir

Nippur—ancient city, home of ✳Enlil

✳**Nirah**—dingir of snakes

✳**Ninsun**—wild cow dingir, mother of Gilgamesh

✳**Nusku**—✳Enlil's steward in the Ekur

Peshtu—Gilgamesh's little sister

✳**Qassutabat**—sweeper of the Land of the Dead

*Sagburu—a wise old woman, avatar of *Inana

Scorpion People—guardians of the Mashu mountains

Shadoof—pole with bucket and counterpoise used for raising water

*Shamash—Akkadian name for *Utu, sun dingir

Shamkat—houri from the house of *Ishtar

Shangashu—hunter who first discovers Enkidu

*Shara—son of *Inana/*Ishtar

Shuruppak—ancient city, home of Ubara-Tutu, birthplace of his son, *Utnapishtim

*Siduri—tavern keeper at the edge of the world

*Silili—dingir mother of horses

*Sippar—city of *Shamash

Sumer—southern region of Mesopotamia

Tigris—easternmost river flowing south through Mesopotamia

Unug—city in Sumer, home of Enmerkar, *Lugalbanda and Gilgamesh; Uruk in Akkadian

Ubara-Tutu—father of *Utnapishtim-the-Far-Away

Uredina—shephard brother of Mashgula

Urgirnuna—a wizard in exile from Hamazi residing in Aratta

Urshanabi—*Utnapishtim's boat-man who journeys across the Sea of Death

Uruk—Akkadian name for Unug

*Utnapishtim-the-Far-Away—king who became immortal after surviving the great flood

*Utu—dingir of the sun

Warka—modern name for the site of the ancient city of Unug/Uruk

Zabu mountains—mountainous region to the east of Sumer
*****Zangara**—dingir of dreams
Zubi mountains—mountainous region somewhere to the east of Sumer

Academic Sources

The Electronic Text Corpus of Sumerian Literature www-etcsl.orient. ox.ac.uk

Thorkild Jacobsen, *The Harps That Once... Sumerian Poetry in Translation*, Yale University Press, 1987

Jeremy Black, Graham Cunningham, Eleanor Robson and Gábor Zólyomi, *The Literature of Ancient Sumer*, Oxford University Press, 2004

Herman Vanstiphout, *Epics of Sumerian Kings—The Matter of Aratta*, Society of Biblical Literature, 2003

Andrew George, *The Epic of Gilgamesh*, Allen Lane, The Penguin Press, 1999

Stephanie Dalley, *Myths from Mesopotamia*, Oxford University Press, 1991

Benjamin R. Foster, *The Epic of Gilgamesh*, W. W. Norton & Company Inc., 2001

150